How Can I Keep From Singing!

Songs and musical activities from around the world for 8–13 year olds

Compiled and edited by
Celia Waterhouse
Lucy Allen
Elspeth Compton
Nandita Hollins

with an introduction and glossary by Celia Waterhouse

with music in mind

reg. charity no. 326552

Preface to 2nd Edition

In this second edition of the BKA Songbook How Can I Keep From Singing!, we have not only made numerous small corrections to the existing text of the book, but we have also undertaken to add new material to update the book for the current teaching climate. Thus users will find at the end of the book Appendix 1 and 2, dealing with the National Curriculum and QCA Guidelines, showing how the songs in this book fulfil the QCA teaching criteria.

In addition an accompanying CD is being planned and recorded, with teachers and choirs from many different schools taking part in the recording. It was decided not to make a CD when the book was first published, in the belief that Kodály-trained teachers know how to access songs from printed copy. But we are keen to make our book truly accessible to all, and have come to realise that in particular visually impaired teachers have no reliable way of learning songs without this aid. We are sure many other teachers, too, will find the CD a useful companion to the new edition. It will be ready later in 2003, and can be ordered through the BKA.

It is two and a half years since the first appearance of the book. It is very good to know that 1,500 copies have now sold, and that these are in skilled hands, in classrooms and teaching rooms up and down the country, and even overseas. It is gratifying to feel that the book is helping to carry forward the aims of the British Kodály Academy.

Celia Waterhouse (for the Songbook Editorial Team)   February 2003

What users have said about How Can I Keep Fron Singing!

"........ *having a resource book to hand with so many lovely songs in it is so helpful. It is full of wonderful new material and useful tips on teaching.*"   (VM, Enfield)

"........*The editors have deliberately avoided the material that crops up in every collection and have tried to find songs to appeal to the 21st century child.*"   (KH, London)

"....... *a real inspiration and valuable resource! I'll be able to put many ideas into action in string teaching and also KS3 classroom teaching.*"   (CD, Cambridge)

2007 Reprint

We have taken the opportunity to update the National Curriculum Appendices (pages 119-123) in line with the latest QCA guidelines. The *Useful Contacts* (page 103) has also been updated).

Addendum

Glossary (see page101)

Accelerando	Getting faster.
Aeolian, Dorian, Mixolydian	The most common modes occurring in British folk song repertoire, ending on la, re and so respectively
Anacrusis	Upbeat. The unstressed note or notes leading into a strong beat.
Da capo or DC al Fine.	From the beginning to Fine (the end). Instruction at the bottom of a piece of music to repeat from the beginning and finish at Fine. Dal segno or DS al Fine: repeat from the sign ($) and finish at Fine.

Words of *This Old Man* (see page 26)

This old man, he played one,
He played nick-nack on my drum.

Nick-nack paddy whack,
Give a dog a bone,
This old man came rolling home.

This old man, he played two,
He played nick-nack on my shoe.

Nick-nack paddy whack etc.

Three - knee
Four - door
Five - hive
Six - sticks
Seven - up in heaven
Eight - plate
Nine - line
Ten - hen

Booklist (see page 104)

Bolkovac, Edward, and Johnson, Judith: *150 Rounds for Singing and Teaching. Boosey and Hawkes.

Geoghegan, Lucinda: * Singing Games and Rhymes for Early Years, *Singing Games and Rhymes for Tiny Tots. National Youth Choir of Scotland

Meek, Bill (compiled by) , 1985. Moon Penny. *A collection of rhymes, songs and play-verse for and by children, gathered in Ireland.* Ossian Publications

Two new books published by the International Kodály Society to mark the 120th Anniversary of the birth of Kodály (December 2002):

Herboly, Ildikó (compiled by): * Music Should Belong to Everyone: 120 quotes by Zoltán Kodály. Parallel text in Hungarian and English.

Hartyányi, Judit (compiled by): * An Ode for Music: 11 analyses of choral compositions of Zoltán Kodály. *A tribute to the composer's legacy of choral music, complete with 2 CDs.*

* Available from BKA Bookstore, see page 103.

About the Authors

Celia Waterhouse (Editorial Team Leader)

Celia trained as a piano teacher after a languages degree. She teaches from her home near Newmarket and at St Faith's School, Cambridge, as well as directing music courses and activities for all ages in Cambridgeshire. She first met the Kodály approach at a workshop with Kodály piano teacher Gillian Earl, and in 1993 started her training with the BKA. It has helped her to appreciate the importance of singing in her own development as a musician from earliest childhood, and to rethink her whole approach to instrumental teaching. Kodály musicianship classes are now an integral part of her practice, and she endeavours to make Kodály's key concept of "musicianship through singing" the cornerstone of her work.

Lucy Allen

Lucy studied piano, oboe and recorder at the Royal Academy of Music. She has taught at secondary, primary and pre-school level, and is currently Director of Music at St Anthony's School, a North London boys' preparatory school. She is Chairman of and principal oboe with the Brent Symphony Orchestra. She began her Kodály training in the early nineties. In her own words: "As a music teacher my search had always been for a method that enabled children to understand the language of music and make it their own, so that skills such as reading, writing, composing and performing, as well as listening, could develop freely and naturally. During my first BKA summer school at Cheltenham in 1991 I knew I had to look no further".

Elspeth Compton

Elspeth studied guitar at the University of Witwatersrand in Johannesburg, and did her Kodály training with the BKA in England. She has taught Kodály at the Royal Northern College of Music on the Junior Strings Project, and for the Guildhall Preparatory Division, and is an Advisory Teacher for the Voices Foundation. She now teaches from her home in Norfolk, working with all ages, from children from age 3 through to adults participating in the Trinity College Certificate of Education. Her mission is to introduce today's children to the fun of singing games, and to watch their transformation as they discover their singing voices.

Nandita Hollins

Dita has studied and taught in India, the USA, Switzerland and England, and has brought a wide repertoire of songs in many languages to the project. She began her teaching career by accident: while training as a concert singer at the Zürich Conservatoire, she was unexpectedly offered a job as Director of Music in a Swiss girl's school, which she accepted. Her subsequent quest to train as a teacher eventually led her to her first Kodály summer school in Ascot in the early eighties, where she found what she had been looking for – a systematic and enjoyable approach to musicianship training through singing. Later, as Head of Music in Harrold Priory Middle School in Bedford, she was able to put Kodály principles to use very successfuly, building up a thriving department and ensuring that music was for everyone in the school. She now works as an Advisory Teacher with the Voices Foundation and as a part-time Lecturer in Primary Music Education at De Montfort University, Bedford.

Contents

Foreword

When Kodály was asked to summarise his educational concept, he said it could be summarised in one word – "singing". Singing is the fundamental way of making music, and the instruments we have devised seek to emulate this ability and extend it. "Only the best material is good enough", said Kodály. Deciding what is best is a more difficult task, but that which has survived the ages (and which has been shaped by those who have treasured it and passed it on) gives us a starting point.

When Kodály began formulating his educational concept and collecting folk-songs, he set himself the task of rescuing Hungarian folk-song before it was lost. More than that, he gave Hungarian culture back to the Hungarians, and he advised teachers and educationalists to look to their national heritage. Today, we face different challenges with our mixed society of different races, languages and creeds from all over the world. In modern Britain we can no longer claim that we should use only British material.

This book rightly reflects the changing nature of our society, and provides some lovely ethnic material, which can have a value far in excess of its value for enjoyment and musicianship training. Such material can make a positive and serious contribution towards fostering racial tolerance and understanding, not only for each individual child, but also for whole nations and races of people. If only politicians and those responsible for developing educational policy could understand this, then our world would begin to become a better place. Kodály recognised this when he said, "Music was one of the most powerful forces in the rise of mankind!.....He who renders it accessible to as many people as possible is a benefactor of humanity".

In my experience we can never have enough singing material, and this new collection will certainly be one which teachers, musicians and educators will find extremely useful. Editing this collection has been a mammoth task for the four editors, and I congratulate them on their efforts. Those who know how to use the material contained here will confirm that their work has really been worth it.

David Vinden, Northwood Hills, May 2000

Acknowledgements

This songbook has arisen from the British Kodály Academy Teachers' Certificate Course (CKME), and many people have contributed to it. Trainee teachers are required to research and start to compile a bank of songs suitable for use in their own Kodály teaching programme. Out of this process an enormous quantity of excellent, highly relevant, and sometimes little known, song material has been discovered, shared and appreciated by CKME students.

The idea of a BKA Millennium Project using this material to produce a songbook was first suggested by Celia Cviić. As Honorary Treasurer of the BKA she has also had a key role in securing the necessary funding. Thus, the songbook owes its existence not only to her vision, but also to her commitment and practical support. CKME Course Director David Vinden's enthusiastic and inspiring teaching has undoubtedly been a major impetus, and the project is further indebted to him for his help and guidance as Consultant. In addition to the many teachers who have contributed song material through the CKME training course and other BKA networks, special thanks are due to BKA members Fiona Gaffney and Judith Brindle. They have been most helpful in making available their own extensive collections of teaching repertoire. Thanks also to Miriam Hughes for advice on Welsh repertoire.

Particular thanks are due to Carole Lindsay-Douglas, BKA patron, Douglas Coombes and Lindsay Music for help and advice on copyright issues and other matters, and for their generous permission to make use of Lindsay Music copyright material. The following people have also helped to bring the book to fruition. Graham Waterhouse has drawn the dance diagrams, and BKA member Tim Bird gave guidance on overall design and created a clear and attractive style for the book. Stephen Adamson took on much of the work of copyright clearance. Kevin Lamb of KL Music and Mike Cole put all the music on disk. Tamsin Cousins, as Production Manager, has coordinated the project, smoothed the way towards publication, and kept tabs on the budget. We are indebted to the Esmée Fairbairn Trust, without whose generous grant the project would have been unable to proceed, and to members of the BKA who have undertaken to raise an additional £2,000 towards production costs.

Lastly, I should like to thank my colleagues on the Editorial Team, Lucy Allen, Elspeth Compton and Dita Hollins. Their wide experience of Kodály work has been a rich source to draw on in the long task of selecting and presenting the songs and related material. We trust our work on this first-ever BKA publication will bring to teachers in the UK a treasure chest of Kodály teaching repertoire and ideas in a practical, accessible and stimulating format.

Celia Waterhouse, February 2000

Introduction

Zoltán Kodály (1882–1967) inspired the development of a systematic and holistic approach to musicianship training in Hungary, from pre-school to diploma level, which has now gained world recognition. This approach, based on unaccompanied singing, makes use primarily of a country's own folk-song material and the best art music. Kodály drew on well-established educational principles, and brought together many practical music education tools that he had observed in use elsewhere. These included relative solfa and hand signs (derived from John Curwen's Tonic Solfa), rhythm solfa (inspired by and simplified from the French rhythm solfa system of Cheve, Gallin and Paris), activity and movement to music (observed in the work of Dalcroze), an early repertoire of pentatonic music to develop strong musical roots, and stick notation, which facilitates sight-reading. These tools are potently combined to establish an in-built sense of pulse, keen pitch discrimination, and a secure grasp of rhythm, as well as developing memory, inner hearing, musical literacy, two-part listening, improvisation skills, coordination, and an understanding of harmony, all essential ingredients for nurturing the whole musician.

Adapted from text by David Vinden

This book of songs and musical activities is both for Kodály enthusiasts, and for junior, middle and lower secondary school teachers, or instrumental teachers, who are interested in the Kodály approach and would like further ideas on how to develop it with groups and classes.

All the songs have been contributed by practising Kodály teachers. In making our selection we have aimed to include songs that we think will be new or unfamiliar to the majority of teachers, as well as a few familiar ones which we believe have particular value for musicianship training. Every song in the book is presented with practical and creative teaching tips showing how to extract the maximum amount of musical learning, challenge and enjoyment from the material. Using this approach even the simplest song becomes a vehicle for extended musicianship work. Indeed, part of the training process for Kodály teachers is to learn to look analytically at songs for their inherent learning potential. The right material, once stored in a child's memory, acts as a seed bed for further musical growth, and it can be returned to many times over for introducing or reinforcing various aspects of musical learning.

Zoltán Kodály believed fundamentally in *music for everyone* because music is such an uplifting experience – "It sheds light on those regions of the soul that cannot be reached by any other means". He also believed that musical literacy is an achievable goal for everyone, and that singing and active music making is the key to musical learning. "Only musical activity can lead someone to an understanding of music . . . simply listening is not enough". Through singing and musical activity we absorb the elements required for music making. This happens unconsciously at first and then, guided by the teacher, consciously, as each element is made explicit and is fitted into the picture at the appropriate time, and given a name and a written symbol. In this way, from the most elementary level to the most advanced, the pupil gradually builds up aural understanding as well as reading skills and a command of the written language of music.

Since it is through songs and rhythmic games that the musical elements are introduced, Kodály teachers are continually looking for good song material to aid that progression from the simplest stages to the most advanced. Our aim in this book is not to present a systematic and sequential Kodály programme for classwork, but to offer varied, practical and enjoyable material. This can either be incorporated into a Kodály programme for 8–13 year olds, or can help teachers think more deeply, perhaps for the first time, about the order in which they present songs to the children they work with. The book shows the potential of each individual song for musicianship training. We have organised our songs into ten sections, which may be a useful model for a Kodály progression, or just a helpful way of finding a song with a particular musical purpose in mind. As a further aid to finding songs there are two indexes at the end of the book: an alphabetical index giving an analytical classification of each song, and a solfa index which lists songs according to the number of solfa pitches they contain.

If you are new to this approach, the early sections (with their simpler songs) present an opportunity for both you, the teacher, and the pupils you are working with to get used to some of the main Kodály teaching tools: solfa syllables (*do re mi* etc), rhythm names (*ta, tete* etc.), hand signs and stick notation. All these are explained more fully below.

Many music teachers and choir trainers mistakenly believe that a piano is an indispensable tool for singing. The piano has traditionally been looked upon as the essential means of conveying a melody, "pulling up" the standard, and keeping everyone together in time and on pitch. There is also a common misconception that a performance is not a "real performance" unless a song is accompanied by the piano. Following Kodály practice we have not included songs in arrangement with piano accompaniment, as there are clearly many other excellent books which do this already. The role of this book is rather to offer teachers an opportunity to work in a different and fulfilling way, in order to allow the singing voice to flourish independently and find a new confidence in itself. In modern Britain, many people are sadly inhibited about opening their mouths and just singing. We hope that teachers, by their own example of leading with the unaccompanied voice, will enable and inspire their pupils to find *their* singing voices, which will be an instrument for music making for the rest of their lives.

We also see our songbook as part of a new creative approach in music education, which we believe is taking hold in this country. It involves taking up for ourselves, as teachers of music at whatever level, both in class music and in instrumental teaching, the tools for musicianship-building and active music making, and putting them also into the hands of the children and young people we work with. In place of piano accompaniment, therefore, we offer ideas and suggestions for creating arrangements or accompaniments in the classroom. This is achieved using rhythmic, vocal or instrumental ostinatos, adding parts in canon, or a bass-line or chord sequence to try on a variety of instruments. Simple rounds, once learned vocally, can be transferred directly to instruments and lend themselves to instrumental group work. The working out, or "arranging", of a song accompaniment with drone bass, simple descant, added ostinato or chord progression may well fulfil a requirement for a composition or improvisation task. Once the songs have been learned in solfa, they can readily be played on instruments in different familiar keys, so it is easy to include transposing instruments such as the clarinet or the trumpet in an ensemble. The possibilities for musicianship work are endless once music teachers wean themselves off the idea that songs are for singing in a choir with a piano accompaniment, that instrumental music has to be different from vocal music, that only the real experts can make musical arrangements, and that simple songs and rounds, folk-songs and traditional ballads have no value except as songs.

Kodály teachers believe the reverse is true. All the great composers have returned again and again to folk-song, traditional melody and the simplest of musical motifs, and have constructed from these building blocks their greatest masterpieces. Kodály based his music education work on traditional Hungarian music and folk-song of the highest quality, which he believed encapsulated the essential ingredients of well-crafted music. We hope, therefore, that music teachers in the UK will find this book a useful and practical resource, whether for extending the Kodály work they already do, for introducing Kodály work into their teaching programme for the first time, or for deepening and broadening their idea of what the Kodály concept is all about.

We introduce below, and throughout the book, some of the key Kodály teaching tools and concepts. Although it is our intention to help teachers to understand something of the Kodály approach, and to give them ideas on how to put it into practice with the children they work with, we would urge them to follow up by going on some of the excellent courses run by the British Kodály Academy and other organisations, whose addresses can be found at the end of this book. There is no substitute for working with top-class tutors from Hungary, the UK and other countries, and the inspiration and practical support teachers gain from both tutors and fellow students is of lasting value.

Tools For Kodály Musicianship

Solfa Names and Hand Signs

Kodály adopted John Curwen's Tonic Solfa system and renamed it *Relative Solfa*. The solfa names do not relate to a fixed pitch, but to a tonal function, ie. *do* for the major tonic and *la* for the minor tonic. Using relative solfa the tonal relationship of notes is made explicit, facilitating understanding of, for example, relative keys, harmonic function or modulation. Relative solfa makes transposition simplicity itself: any music understood in solfa can be sung at any pitch, or played in any key the player is conversant with. It is also the key to understanding of pentatonic scales and the modes, the forerunners of modern scales, some of which are introduced with songs in this book.

This book uses the Italianate spelling of the solfa syllables (*do*, *re*, *mi* etc.), rather than the traditional British spelling (*doh*, *ray*, *me* etc.). The simpler spellings encourage singing on a pure vowel sound rather than a diphthong, and this is better both for voice production and clarity of intonation. The solfa names can also be abbreviated to their initial letters (*d r m* etc.).

The Relative Solfa hand signs help to develop the inner hearing by acting as a visual and spatial reminder of the solfa sound being imagined or sung. Teachers and conductors can use them as an aid for cueing notes and for intonation work. Children and students should also be taught and encouraged to use them, as the physical gesture is a tangible reminder of the required pitch, and helps them to reproduce it accurately.

If you are new to solfa and hand signs, build up gradually, starting with songs with a limited tone-set or stepwise melody. When working with young beginners, Kodály teachers usually begin with *so–mi*, the spontaneous "coo-ee" singing pitches that are used for calling someone's name. This is the starting point for building up the whole pentatonic (or five sounds) scale:

do   *re*   *mi*   *so*   *la*   *do'*

Much Hungarian, and some British, folk-music is pentatonic. The pentatonic scale contains no semitones, and Kodály believed that in beginning with the pentatone, secure tuning is established. Later the diatonic scale is introduced:

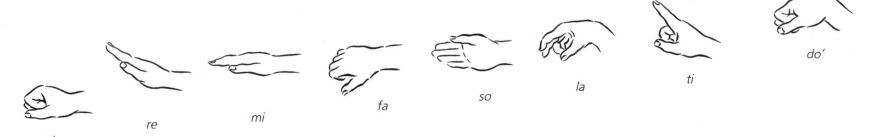

do   *re*   *mi*   *fa*   *so*   *la*   *ti*   *do'*

The songs in this book use mainly the pentatonic and diatonic notes above. A few songs contain the chromatic notes *di, fi, si,* and *ta:* *

do – di   fa – fi   so – si   ta – ti

Rhythmic Solfa

To support the learning and accurate performance of rhythm, Kodály adapted the French time names which convey the relative length or duration of musical sounds. Like the relative solfa names, the time names *are* the sounds required, and as such act as a potent reminder of the note length. Some music teachers have great success with using other mnemonics to recall musical rhythms to mind: words are indeed a most valuable aide-mémoire for rhythms, and the combination of words and music is acknowledged as a powerful means of learning and of training the memory. However, the advantage of rhythmic solfa is that it is simple to learn and apply, systematic and logical; rhythmic solfa acts as a universal common denominator.

The rhythm names† we have adopted in this book are:

| ta (Long vowel as in *bath*) | ta-a | ta-a-a | ta-a-a-a | ta-e | sh |

| te te (Short vowel as in *bed*) | ta-e te | te ta-e | te ta te (*syncopa*) | tri o la |

| ti ri ti ri | ti ri te | te ti ri | tem - ri | ti - rem |

For 𝟔/𝟖 *rhythms please see the Teaching Tips on page 9 (Deryn y bwn).*

As with learning a foreign language, the rhythm words will be fully internalised and understood only when *spoken aloud.* Likewise, only when musical motifs are clapped rhythmically and accurately will they be fully assimilated as preparation for musical performance. Only by *actively engaging* with rhythms in this way, as a regular part of musicianship training will they be completely learned.

* *Note: there are slight variations to the chromatic note hand signs among Kodály practitioners.*

† *Note: there are slight variations to these words among Kodály teachers. The rhythm names above follow the principle of a shorter vowel to indicate a shorter note.*

Time names have no rhythmic meaning unless they are part of a musical motif or phrase: their length can only be defined and understood *in relation* to other notes. As with solfa names, the rhythm names are introduced gradually, starting with *ta*, *tete* and *sh*. From the earliest stages, Kodály teachers use rhythm flash cards to reinforce the learning of rhythms and to develop the visual memory and musical reactions of their pupils. Continuous rhythmic performance is the most essential ingredient of good sight-reading, and it is impossible to achieve it without a reliable understanding of rhythm.

It is helpful to teach children "musical clapping" for the purposes of such exercises. For *ta* and shorter values, there is one "working hand" (usually the right hand) and one "steady hand", making for a more relaxed action than will occur when children try to coordinate both hands in faster clapping. For values longer than *ta*, after the initial clap the hands remain clasped, marking each crotchet pulse rhythmically without undue stress. For the crotchet rest, the hands are separated, and the pulse is marked with an open gesture, palms up.

Obvious as it may seem, it needs to be stated that rhythm is a more fundamental ingredient of music than melody. Children who find the *clapping* of certain rhythms difficult will inevitably experience difficulty when *playing* these rhythms as melodic motifs on instruments. Children who "clap-and-say" rhythms as a regular part of their learning develop a secure and integrated grasp of rhythm for musicianship work, singing or instrumental work. Conversely, it is possible for students to achieve advanced levels of performance without this training, but also without the inner understanding, rhythmic accuracy and internalised musicianship which Kodály teachers strive to nurture in all their students.

Stick Notation

For a quick rhythm shorthand most notes can be simplified to their sticks alone, this being the part conveying distinctive information about duration. A crotchet rest can be abbreviated to ⸜ , the top part of the full rest symbol. Only minims and longer values need to be written in full to be understood. The filled-in note-heads and the full crotchet rest symbol are the most time-consuming parts to write, especially by children, so this shorthand is very useful for musicianship work, and it is both clear and precise:

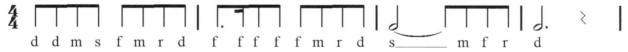

Written rhythms can be combined with solfa to create a concise means of transcribing a melody commonly known as *stick notation*. It is used by Kodály teachers before stave notation is introduced, and it remains a tool for musicianship work even after stave reading is established.

Stave notation is a compact and sophisticated encoding of complex musical information. Each note symbol conveys several different meanings, and in addition has to be interpreted in the context of general instructions about pitch, metre, tempo and key, likewise encoded at the head of the music or at various points along the page. Stave notation, even at its simplest, conveys far more information visually than stick notation. In the early stages much of this is lost on students, who generally see only one or two symbols at a time and are unable to remember all the encoded information simultaneously. This can quickly lead to disenchantment and a sense of failure. It is little wonder, then, that so many people in Britain regard the ability to read music as the realm of the talented few, and that sight-reading is such an ordeal to most young musicians, as well as a good many older ones.

Kodály teachers consider the process of learning to read music as a central part of musical training, too important to leave to chance. As with learning to read language, it requires a step-by-step approach, and each stage has to be actively practised until it is secure enough to be a stepping stone to the next stage. Kodály believed that "bad reading is mainly caused by rhythmic clumsiness and hesitation" and that "rhythm is always of the greatest importance". Stick notation is a tool that can be used on the way to learning to read music fluently, as it helps beginners to bypass some of the confusions of stave reading, and enables them instead to focus clearly on the rhythm patterns in association with the relative solfa pitches.

As well as being a valuable aid for learning to read music, stick notation has many other advantages. It is one of the quickest and simplest ways of notating music, far quicker than stave notation, and thus is a time-saving way of writing music on the board, or taking down a musical dictation. Look at the examples below and draw your own conclusions:

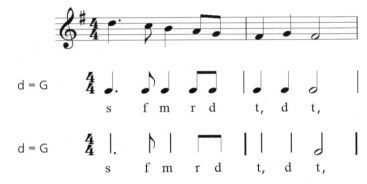

In addition, and perhaps even more importantly, stick notation enables the inner hearing to develop, as the sounds have to be imagined in the head before the music can be sung. It is important, therefore, to ensure that children always *clap* and *sing* from the stick notation to learn and internalise the rhythms and pitches, before trying out a melody on instruments, which can bypass the inner hearing.

Stick notation is also a very practical tool for reinforcing familiarity with different keys, as well as for transposition. Music in stick notation can be transferred to stave, or sung on letter names or played on instruments, in whatever keys need to be practised or to suit the demands of a particular voice range or transposing instrument. Indeed, once teachers become conversant with it themselves, they cannot fail to realise its simplicity, and its great potential for musicianship work.

Many of the songs in the early sections of this book are given in stick notation as well as stave notation, and teachers not yet familiar with using stick notation and relative solfa can use this as an opportunity to try it for themselves.

Easy Songs in Major Keys

We have deliberately started this book with some very easy material. If you are already a Kodály practitioner, you will be familiar with the style of the musicianship exercises and singing games presented here. None the less, we hope you will find a few new ideas! If it is all new to you, we offer these songs as an opportunity to get used to Kodály ways of working. Practise using solfa pitch syllables (*do re mi* etc), time names (*ta, tete,* etc) and hand signs, until you feel confident with them. Once these are integrated into your everyday way of working, you will begin to see what versatile and practical tools they are.

The most important and fundamental component of music is the pulse which holds everything together in a rhythmic cohesion. The ability to feel the pulse while singing or listening to music is the cornerstone on which all musical understanding is built. We make no apology for urging you to build up a repertoire of games and activities that develops the sense of pulse. Get into the habit of making the children clap, patsch and walk the beat as part of the process of learning any new song. It is time well spent, because the sense of pulse is a prerequisite for any more complex musical activity, such as clapping an ostinato rhythm or holding a part in a round.

Four American Traditional Songs

Many American songs are not well known in Britain and have much potential for developing musicianship skills. Before trying the singing games, make sure the children can clap the pulse as they sing, and that they can also clap the word rhythms.

Love Somebody

American traditional

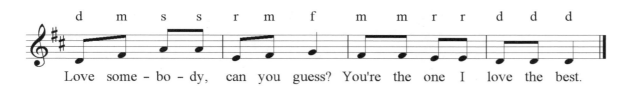

Teaching Tips

■ Useful material for working on the first five steps of the scale (*do* pentachord).
Try it in stick notation:

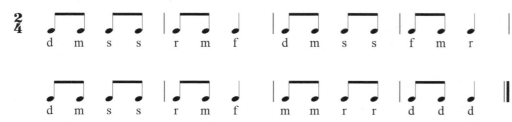

■ A good piece for young pianists to try. Once they know it, they can have fun making up an accompaniment using *d*, and *s*,.

Circle Game

(standing or seated on chairs):

The children hold both hands in front of them, palms up.

■ A chosen child moves round the inside of the circle patting each pair of hands with each ♩ (*ta*) beat.

■ On the last line s/he stays with the same partner, and both children clap the last three words:

love the best

■ The children swap places for the game to continue.

Alabama Gal

American traditional

Al - a - ba - ma gal, won't you come out to - night?

come out to - night? come out to - night?

Al - a - ba - ma gal, won't you come out to - night, And

dance by the light of the moon?

Teaching Tips

■ Take care to sing the full length of ♩ (*ta-a*) at the ends of phrases.

■ ♪ ♩ ♪ (*syncopa*) is a prominent rhythmic feature. Get half the group to clap this ostinato:

Come out to-night

while the other half sings the song. (Getting them to do both these things at once takes a lot of hard work!)

■ Develop pulse and rhythm by letting one child walk the ♩ pulse inside the circle while all the others clap the word rhythms as they sing.

■ Simple Circle Dance
Form a circle with pairs of children holding cross-hands, facing anti-clockwise for promenade (see diagram).

– 1st and 2nd lines: Partners walk around the circle for 8 ♩ beats.

– 3rd line: Facing partner, clap hands, then patsch partner's hands (x2).

– 4th line: Everyone takes two sidesteps to the right to change partners for the next time.

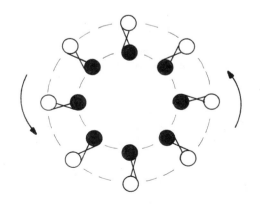

3

Grandma Grunts

American traditional

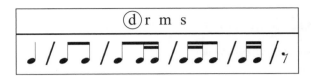

1. Grand - ma Grunts said a cu-ri-ous thing, "Boys may whis-tle but girls must sing."

That is what I heard her say. 'Twas no long-er than yes-ter-day.

Boys can whis-tle, (whistle - -) Girls must sing "Tra la-la-la-la."

2 Boys can whistle, of course they may,
They can whistle the live-long day.
Why can't girls whistle too, pray tell,
If they manage to do it well?
Boys can whistle etc

3 Grandma Grunts said it wouldn't do,
Gave a very good reason too:
Whistling girls and crowing hens
Always come to some bad ends.
Boys can whistle etc

■ This is a useful song for working with stick notation:

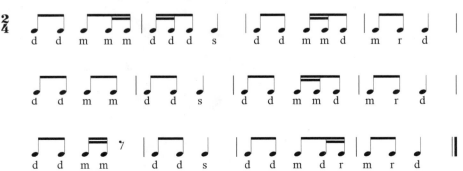

Teaching Tips

■ Melodic motifs include *d–m d–s* and *m–r–d*. Ask the children to listen as you sing the song, and to put up their hands when they hear one of these motifs chosen by you. (Start with *m–r–d*, which comes at the end of a line and so is more prominent.)

■ As you sing, stop on certain notes and get them to sing back the solfa name with handsign.

■ Each line is a variation of the first line. Write the rhythm on the board and see if the children can tell you the solfa names for the first line. After working together on line 1, see if the children can work out the rest of the solfa on their own.

■ The words may be amusing, but the message is out of step with current thinking. Talk about how and why times have changed, and have fun with the song changing around the boys' and girls' roles.

■ This ostinato works well with the song:

Grand-ma Grunts, Grand-ma Grunts

Make up other ostinatos in stick notation, using rhythms and notes from the song.

■ Try it as a canon. Start group 2 at the second bar. Make sure everyone is in tune on *d*.

Sweep Away

American traditional

Teaching Tips

■ For children who can already sight-sing, this song provides useful sight-reading material, with its stepwise and tonic chord-based intervals.

■ Very good for *cantabile* singing. Try dividing it phrase by phrase between a group and a soloist/semi-chorus. (Start off the first phrase with the group singing.)

■ You can make a beautiful two-part arrangement by adding a second part in canon, beginning from the upbeat to bar 5. Let the second voice follow on, starting with this phrase a bar behind.

Salut, Ça Va?

Words and Music by Nandita Hollins

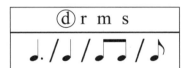

Teaching Tips

■ A very easy song, useful for cross-curricular work. Tie it in with first-year French. Translate it into English!

■ *s–m* is the usual starting point for introducing work on solfa. You might find this song helpful for making conscious the first solfa syllables.

■ This is another good song for working with stick notation. See if the children can sing it from this notation:

Who Stole my Chickens?

Traditional

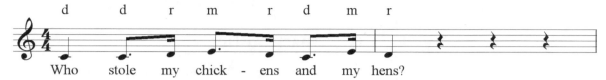

d   d   r   m   r   d   m   r

Who stole my chick - ens and my hens?

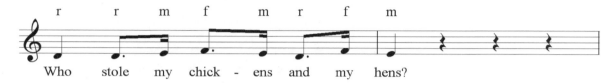

r   r   m   f   m   r   f   m

Who stole my chick - ens and my hens?

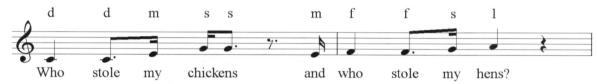

d   d   m   s   s   m   f   f   s   l

Who stole my chickens and who stole my hens?

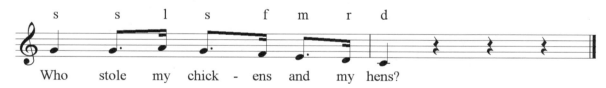

s   s   l   s   f   m   r   d

Who stole my chick - ens and my hens?

Teaching Tips

■ Useful for learning the 🎵 (*temri*) rhythm. Practise clapping the word rhythms for crisp performance.

■ Take this further with stick notation. Sing the solfa from the board or OHP and clap the rhythms.

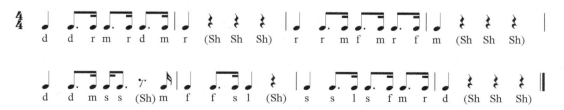

d d r m r d m r (Sh Sh Sh) r r m f m r f m (Sh Sh Sh)

d d m s s (Sh) m f f s l (Sh) s s l s f m r d (Sh Sh Sh)

■ Have some fun working on rests with this song:

1. Clap the pulse through the song to discover the rest beats. Pay special attention to the third line, where the 🎵 upbeat after the 𝄽 rest may cause some problems.

2. "Pass" the clap from child to child around the circle ("hocketing") as you sing again.

3. Sing with "thinking voice" (silently with inner hearing) and this time clapping *just* the rests.

4. "Share" the song around the circle like this (very good for concentration!):

   – first child sings first phrase

   – next three children hocket the three rests

   – next child sings second phrase

   – etc.

■ Make up some new verses which give opportunities for short solos:

"You stole......"   "I stole........"   (or adding the children's names instead).

6

Oi Dana

Polish dance song

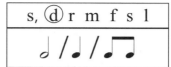

Oi da - na, oi da - na Oi da - na, oi da - na.

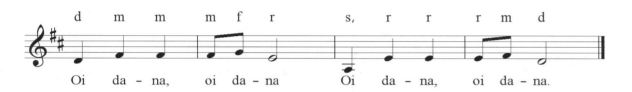

Oi da - na, oi da - na Oi da - na, oi da - na.

Teaching Tips

■ You can use this song to reinforce the understanding of 3-time. Teach by rote, feeling the pulse on the knees, and find the strong beat. Let the children discover in this way how many beats there are in a bar, then show them how to mark beats 2 and 3 with a lighter clap, which helps them feel the lilting rhythm of the song.

■ Discuss what sort of a song this is (a lullaby), and decide on a suitable tempo and dynamics. Sing it to the word "Lullaby".

■ The song is in ABAC form, but the rhythm remains the same for every phrase. Using the given rhythm, get the children to compose different melodies in the B and C sections. Stick notation is very helpful for working on this kind of exercise.

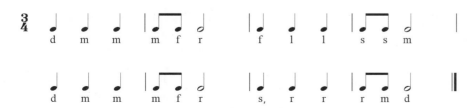

Two Welsh Folk-Songs

d r m f s l t (d') r' m'

There is a wealth of Welsh folk-song material little known outside of Wales. As well as being a rich tradition that is well worth exploring, many of the songs are excellent for musicianship work in Junior and Middle schools. Nowadays the trend is for songs to be sung in their language of origin. We give them here in Welsh, with a pronunciation guide as well as the English translation. Children are refreshingly open minded about trying songs in different languages, which to them seem no harder than some of the nonsense syllables found in our traditional song repertoire.

Hen wraig fach yn bywyn y Cwm, Di-llad car-piog a chloc-sie trwm. Roedd
Hair-n oor-aye-g v-are-ch* un* biw un er coomb Di-ll-add* car-pee-og arech-locks-yer troo-mRoy-th

gan-ddi lo o'r e nw Twm, Un ti-la iawn ers ta-lwm.
gan-thee lo oar en-oo Tom E'en til-ah yawn e'ers tal-oom

Dim di-dl dim di-dl dim dim dim, Dim di-dl dim di-dl dim dim dim. Di-dl

dim di-dl dim di-dl dim di-dl dim di-dl dim dim dim dim dim dim.

* Pronunciation Guide

ch = gargling sound (back of throat)

un = as in <u>un</u>der

di = as in <u>di</u>m

ll = Welsh pronunciation as in <u>Ll</u>andrindod

Hen Wraig Fach (A little old lady)

Welsh folk-song, words by Llew Jones.
Published by permission of the Welsh Folk Song Society

Teaching Tips

- With its stepwise melody, this is an excellent song for working on the whole scale. Try it in stick notation:

d' d' d' d' t l l s   l l l l s f m d
r m f s   l t d' r'   m' s l t   d' d'

- Especially useful for ♩♫ (*te tiri*). Ask the children to count how many times they hear this rhythm while you sing the song.

- Get the children to listen for rhythmic patterns from different bars of the song, eg:

tete tete   te ti ri ta   tete te ti ri

ta ta   te ti ri te ti ri   tete ta

They can try these out as ostinatos with clapping or untuned percussion.

- Learn to pronounce the Welsh sounds, just as you would learn words of any new song, before you try teaching them in class.

Translation

A little old lady lived down the valley. She wore tattered clothes and heavy clogs. She had a calf called Twm, which had been looking old for a while.

The little old lady gave the calf some milk but he refused to take it. Well, she went out of her mind, and there was such a commotion.

Deryn y Bwn o'r Banna (The Bittern from the Beacons)

There is so much 𝄞 material in British folk, nursery and playground songs and games that it is good to do some groundwork in making it conscious at a fairly early stage. You can do some very useful rhythm work with this song.

Welsh folk-song. Published by Permission of the Welsh Folk Song Society

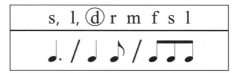

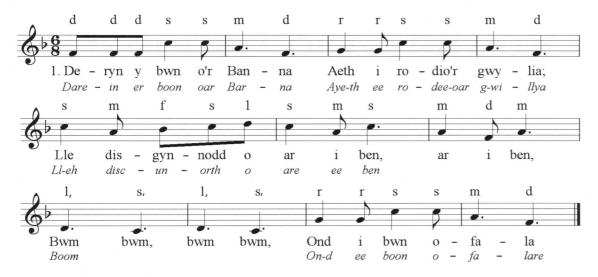

Pronunciation Guide

2 Deryn y Bwn a gododd
   are go-dor-th

Y fala i gyd a gariodd
Er val-are ee g-ee-d are gar-ee-o-th

Dros y Banna
Dr-or-s er Bar-na

i farchnad Caer, i farchnad Caer
ee var-ch-nad K-ayer

Ac yno'n dae'r fe'u gwerthodd.
Ack un-or-n dai'r ver-ee goo-er-th-or-th

Translation

A bittern from the Beacons went for a trip during the holidays. He fell headlong into a heap of apples.

The bittern got up and carried all the apples over the Beacons to Carmarthen market where he sold them.

Apples, thousands of yellow apples. The children loudly demanded apples. They gave only a halfpenny for hundreds.

The bittern returned home over the Beacons. He shouted "See the money I have for selling apples".

Teaching Tips

■ Make a set of 𝄞 rhythm flashcards with the basic 𝄞 patterns.

– See how many of the flashcard rhythms the children can hear in the song.

– Use the flashcard rhythms as individual or combined ostinato patterns while singing this and other 𝄞 songs

– Put up a row of four cards. The class claps this as a repeating sequence all the way through the song.

■ This song is unusual in its irregular phrase lengths. Discuss the phrasing pattern, and let the children "discover" the three-bar phrase in the middle.

2 Very Easy Rounds and Canons

Rounds and canons are an instant way into part singing. They spring in abundance from the early vocal traditions of Britain and many other European countries, as well as going right to the heart of Kodály work.

Rounds and canons need no instrumental accompaniment, creating as they do a beautiful tapestry of interwoven harmony from a single melody line. Enjoy them for their simplicity, admire them for their complexity, and delight in their perfect unity.

Keep Music Alive

Words and music by Douglas Coombes. Published by kind permission of Lindsay Music

Chocolate Cake

Attributed to Ruth Edwards

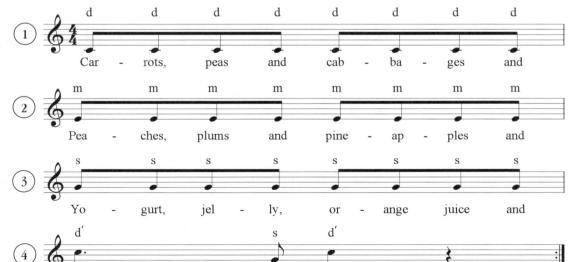

Teaching Tips

■ This is a great song for unconsciously absorbing the syncopated rhythm which occurs at the end of each phrase.

■ Teach by rote, and make sure the long note at the end of each line lasts right to the end of the bar. Get the children to keep their mouths on an open "Ah" shape all the way through this syllable for a pure vowel sound.

Teaching Tips

■ This round is an exciting build-up of the notes of the *do* chord (*d–m–s–d'*). Try it in stick notation:

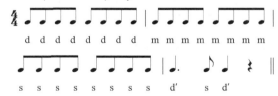

■ Once learned, use it to help the children practise different keys: sing it on letter-names, and write it on the stave.

■ It is sometimes useful to try a four-part round with only three voices. This gives a different arrangement of chords with each line. In this song you can pause on the first note of each line to hear this difference.

11

For Health and Strength

The British Guide Association

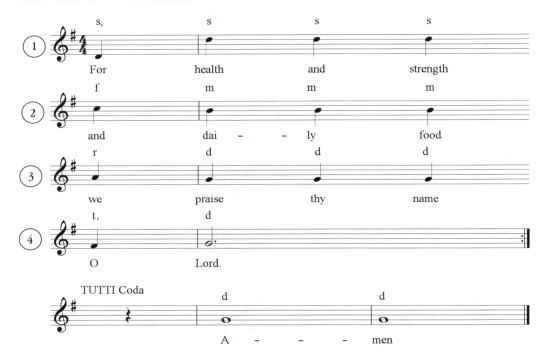

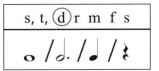

Teaching Tips

■ Both these rounds are useful for reinforcing the steps of the scale.

■ When sung on solfa, they point the way to chord-building.

■ Good material for dictation, and for work with stick notation.

For All Thy Good Gifts

C. Benoit

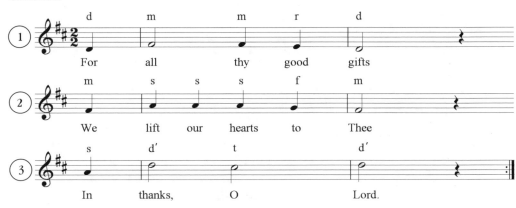

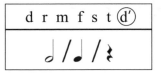

Christmas Round

Anon.

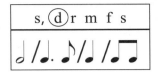

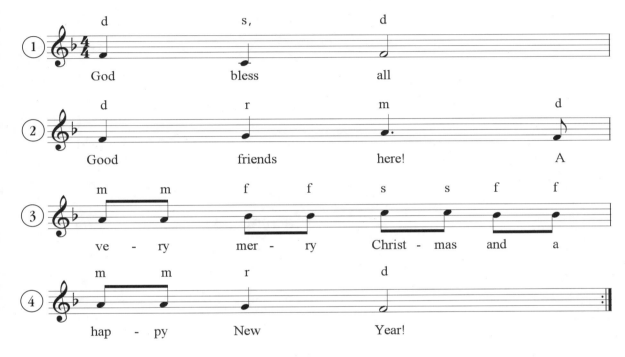

Teaching Tips

- A simple seasonal round. Teach by rote at the end of a Christmas concert, and get parents to join in.

- Use ‖: ♩ ♩ ♩. :‖ as an ostinato accompaniment.
  d s, d
  God bless all

This would sound best in a low range, so give this part to the dads!

- Useful for work with stick notation:

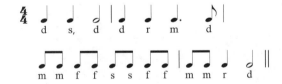

13

Sing Together Merrily

Most rounds are in three or four parts. Here is one in five – a new challenge for children.

Traditional

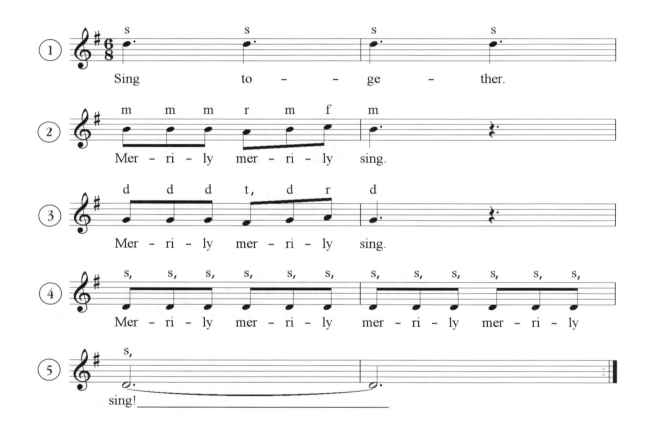

Teaching Tips

■ This round builds a major triad downwards starting with *s* as the top note and ending with *s,* at the bottom. Use it for making conscious the intervals in the major triad as the parts build:

   s–m minor third

   m–d major third

   d–s, perfect fourth

■ Good introduction to compound time ($\frac{6}{8}$) as its rhythm consists of only the ♩. (*ta-e*) pulse beat and the full bar of quavers (♫♫ ♫♫).

Solfa Canon

Lajos Bárdos. Copyright Editio Musica Budapest 1970

Teaching Tips

■ There are no words here: singing on the solfa syllables fixes them in the memory and builds fluency and confidence.

■ This is a very good example of the falling fifth (*d'–f*), which is a difficult interval to learn.

■ Start singing the canon and let the class follow a bar behind. This is an excellent way of developing two-part listening, and a challenge for the memory.

Solfège Round

Solfège is the word for musicianship and singing exercises using the solfa syllables.

Anon.

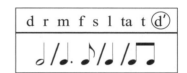

Teaching Tips

■ This is harder to sing than the previous song, but for learning intervals in a major scale it can't be beaten!

■ Teach by rote and memorise. Stick notation is useful here.

Sing on letter names in different keys.

15

Ho! Every Sleeper Waken

Traditional

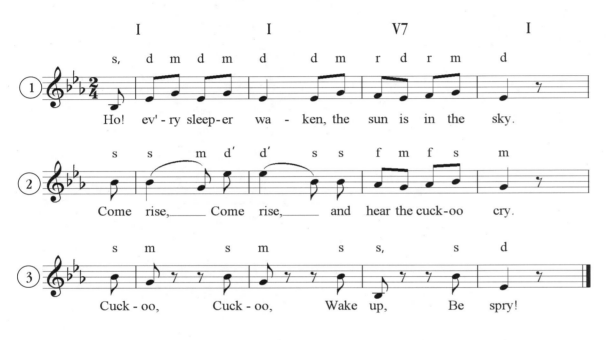

Teaching Tips

■ Use solfa as an aid to practising and analysing the intervals abundant in this song. Point out all the leaps on the notes of the *do* chord.

■ To make the rests in the last line very well defined, echo the words with "listening voice" (silently with inner hearing).

■ The chord pattern of the round is I, I, V7, I. Add a vocal or instrumental accompaniment using notes from these chords. Start with a very simple rhythm, and then get the children to try out their own rhythmic ideas, eg:

(The rhythm of the rests in the last line.)

Senua de Dende (Canon)

In this traditional call and response song, a mother is calling for her child, using a pet-name.

Ghanaian folk-song

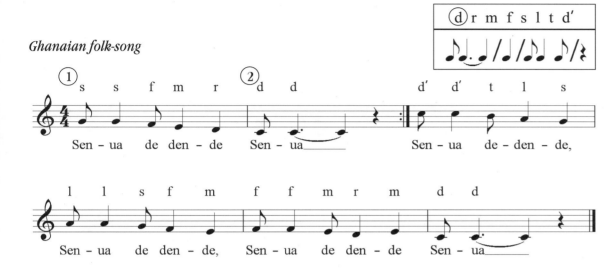

Teaching Tips

- Another stepwise song. Start in canon at the second bar.

- Very good for reinforcing ♪♪♩ ♪ (*syncopa*). Perform an action on the 𝄽 rest.

- Try this ostinato clap: 𝄆 ♩. ♪ ♫ ♩ 𝄇

Praise Him

Traditional gospel

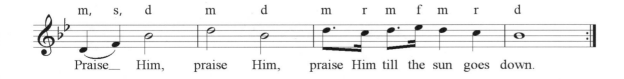

Teaching Tips

- A four-part canon with lots of scope for working on the notes of the *do* chord.

- The first bar is a useful introduction to a *do* chord in first inversion (*m,–s,–d*), and could be compared with *d,–m,–s,* or root position. Let three groups or individual voices sing the three notes together as a block chord, changing from root to first inversion and back, so that everyone can hear the difference in the sound. This will be good preparation for identifying chords and their inversions in higher aural tests of music practical exams.

- Discuss the more relaxed atmosphere of swing rhythm, and the effect it has on the ♩. ♪ rhythm. This is an opportunity for looking at where swing rhythm is appropriate in vocal music and where it isn't. Listen to some jazz or gospel.

17

Two Canons by Michael Praetorious (1571–1604)

Many churches and some school halls provide the right accoustics to bring out the best in these beautiful canons.

Alleluia

Michael Praetorious

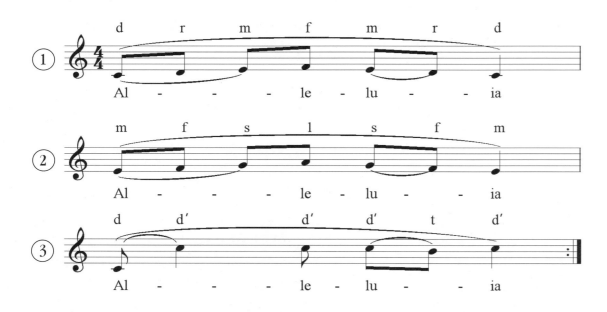

- Useful for work in stick notation:

Teaching Tips

■ The melody has a simple stepwise sequence in the first two phrases, followed by an octave leap (*d–d'*). This presents a special challenge here, combined with the ♪♩ ♪ (*syncopa*) rhythm.

■ Use in various ways for developing vocal technique:

– Sing staccato from the diaphragm, and feel the movement by holding the hand lightly over the abdomen.

– To relax the muscles in the throat on the octave leap, bend the knees as you sing *d'*.

– This canon needs a beautiful *legato*. To get a clear *legato* sound, tell the children to sing like honey pouring from a spoon.

Viva la Musica

Michael Praetorious

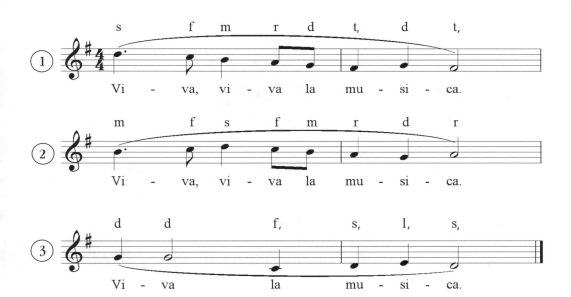

Teaching Tips

■ Useful for the dotted rhythm ♩. ♪ (*ta-e te*). It also has a good example of ♩ ♩. ♩ (*ta ta-a ta*), which is an augmented version of ♪♩ ♪ (*syncopa*).

■ Another example of a falling fifth (*d–f,*), which lays good foundations for hearing the basic harmonic progressions in a bass line.

19

3 Response and Echo Songs

One of the objectives of singing games and songs is to develop musical independence in the children, so that they can make decisions about tempo, dynamics and pitch, and have the confidence to initiate an activity.

Response and echo songs are ideal for this purpose, and lay important groundwork for later participation at a more advanced level in ensemble work, as well as giving relevant early experience to would-be young conductors.

Che Che Kule

The arrangement of intervals in this song make a very African sound, reminiscent of pygmy yodelling and some African birdsong. *Che* is pronounced like the beginning of the word <u>ch</u>air.

Ghanaian children's song

Teaching Tips

■ Teach to the children by rote: you sing, they respond.

■ Every phrase has a different rhythm. Put each rhythm onto a flashcard and get the children to read and clap.

■ Decide on a strong action to perform on the pulse, to be used throughout the song.

■ Invite other action suggestions from the children and try them out. Choose five, one for each phrase, and decide on the order. Remembering the sequence becomes an enjoyable challenge and keeps the children alert. When they are confident in the responses, they can take turns at being the leader and deciding on an action sequence.

■ The song uses only three different pitches from the pentatonic scale, *s*, *l*, and *d*. Within this limited toneset, using solfa to help them, the children can explore the various combinations of intervals and the changing melodies this produces:

   s,–l, major 2nd   *l,–d* minor 3rd   *s,–d* perfect 4th

Let them choose their own three pitches from the pentatonic scale and see how many melodies they can make up. Start with some simple rhythms, or use the rhythms from the song. More able children will enjoy inventing their own.

Everywhere We Go

This is a fun song playing with dynamics, and the topic is dear to everyone's heart: "You'd better listen!".

Traditional chant

Teaching Tips

■ As the range of the song is not very wide, it gives the leader the opportunity to change the starting note, and the followers to match it by listening carefully.

■ Talk about getting louder with control. Discuss the difference between shouting and loud singing. You can also go the other way, controlling getting softer and whispering.

■ Play with tempo, singing faster or slower.

■ These simple tunes are excellent preparation for the sight-singing in AB Grade 4 Aural Tests. Try them first with solfa, and then sing on letter-names in the keys of C, G and F major.

* *Last time: replace the last two bars with (spoken): "We say, you'd better LISTEN!"*

Missa Ram Goat

This is an echo song with the added difficulty that the phrases are overlapping: as the echo is being sung the new phrase is started. The bonus is the resulting two-part harmony.

Jamaican folk–song, words and arrangement by Tom Murray.
© Oxford University Press, 1952. Reproduced by permission. Licence no. 05236

Teaching Tips

■ It is quite hard to fit this song together in two parts. The easiest approach is to leave out the "*Barba deh ya!*" refrain to start with, and teach the rest of the song as call and echo, first with you as the leader, and later in two groups. When this is secure, get a third group to add the "*Barba deh ya!*" as an ostinato throughout. Let everyone have a turn at being in this ostinato group: this will lay the foundations for putting the two parts together.

■ In spite of its apparent complexity the song has only three easy phrases, which you can reinforce by working on them with solfa and stick notation:

■ The "*Barba deh ya*" refrain reinforces the feel of ♪♩ ♪ (*syncopa*), and later you can make this rhythm conscious.

■ Compare with the more straightforward *Hill and Gully Rid-a* (see Stocks and Maddocks, 1992, *Growing with Music* KS2 Book A). This song uses the same pentatonic tone set and has a similar melody. Teach the easier song first as a foundation, or use it as sight-reading material after working on *Missa Ram Goat*.

Ma, Ma, Will You Buy Me a Banana?

Canadian singing game

d' s f f m s d m m r f t, r r d m s

Ma, Ma, will you buy me a, will you buy me a, will you buy me a,
(Ma) Yes, yes, ⸕ I'll buy you a, ⸕ I'll buy you a, ⸕ I'll buy you a,

d' s f f m s d m m r f t, r d d

Ma, Ma, will you buy me a, will you buy me a ba-na-na?
Yes, yes, ⸕ I'll buy you a, ⸕ I'll buy you a ba-na-na.

2 Ma, ma, will you peel the skin, etc.
(Ma) Yes, yes, I'll peel the skin, etc.

3 Ma, ma, do you want a bite? etc.
(Ma) Yes, yes, I'll have a bite etc.

4 Ma, ma, you greedy thing!
You greedy thing! You greedy thing!
Ma, ma, you greedy thing!
You've eaten my banana!

Ma, ma, will you buy me a, etc.

Teaching Tips

■ This is a delightful song for having fun with role-play, and gives a great incentive to the children to sing a short solo.

■ If you are working with children who are not yet confident enough to start on *d'*, teach the easier version of the song with *s* as the first note. The rest of the song is the same.

■ To hold the attention of the rest of the group while the soloists are singing, get the others to perform different actions on the pulse, one for the child and one for the mother.

24

4 Easy Part Songs

Part-singing is fundamental to the Kodály concept: Kodály believed that true intonation can only come through part-singing, and that children should sing in parts from the earliest possible stage. Fundamental to all two-part work is the ability to feel the pulse. Hence the insistence in the Kodály approach on activities which encourage this: rhythmic actions on the pulse, use of rhythmic ostinatos, and response and echo songs. Rounds and canons, melodic ostinatos, use of augmentation, and quodlibets, provide further valuable material to develop these skills through enjoyable singing, while at the same time starting to work on intonation and two-part listening skills. Through use of solfa, the children become aware of true intervals and learn to adjust their tuning by using their own ears and voices. They are now ready for more independent part-singing.

When teaching part-songs, let the whole group learn to sing both (or all) parts. In this way, the children experience and understand more fully all that is going on simultaneously. Use of solfa makes for very secure learning of parts, so it is worth all the time spent on it. It also lays foundations for hearing and understanding harmony. At a later stage this can be made conscious, and the hearing will be already in place for recognising cadences and harmonic progressions, as required for AB Grade 5 Theory and Grade 6–8 aural tests.

This Old Man

Most British children learn this song at Infants School. Since it is so well-known, we are presenting it here in stick notation in an original arrangement. As a preparation, make sure the children have marched to the song and clapped the pulse.

Traditional children's counting song, arranged by Geoffry Russell-Smith. Reproduced with permission of Boosey & Hawkes, © 1978

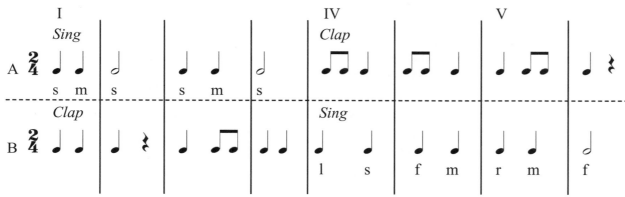

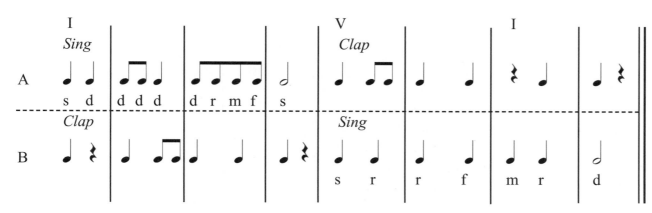

Teaching Tips

- See how quickly the children recognise the song when they try it from the stick notation.

- Practise each part separately before performing together, slowly and carefully at first, then try increasing the tempo.

- The song is more usually notated in notes of half the value, ie:

Get the children to transcribe it in this way as a written exercise (cf. AB Theory Grade 2). They can also write it out in stave notation in whatever keys they need to practise.

- An excellent song for instrumental work.
  - Divide the melody as shown between groups.
  - Add percussion accompaniment on the given rhythms, or new ones invented by the children.
  - Add a bass-line on the beat, or a chordal accompaniment, using chords I, IV and V.

Mountain Hike

To perform this song, divide the class into two groups, representing two groups of hikers climbing opposite sides of a Swiss mountain. Everyone needs to learn both melodies, which are easily taught by rote with the aid of solfa and hand signs.

Swiss Girl Guide song

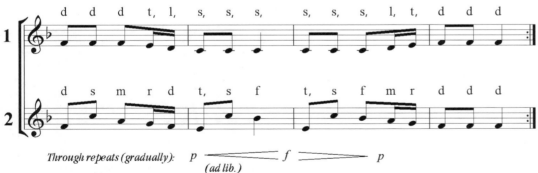

Suggested Performance

Start Group I, then bring in Group II, both *piano*.
(*The hikers begin their climb*).

Keeping the same melodies, the groups *crescendo* gradually to *forte*.
(*The hikers meet at the summit*).

They now swap melodies and begin a *diminuendo.....*
(*They make their descent down the opposite side*)

.....to *piano* and fade out.

Teaching Tips

■ A good song for the unconscious learning of tonic and dominant harmonies (chords I and V), as well as for controlling a gradual *crescendo* and *diminuendo*.

Down the River

Traditional

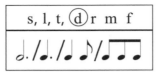

s, l, t, (d) r m f

1 s, s, s, s, s, l, l, l, l, l, t, t, t, l, t, d r m

Down the ri - ver oh down the ri - ver oh down the ri - ver we go, we go.

s, s, s, s, s, l, l, l, l, l, t, t, t, l, t, d

Down the ri - ver oh down the ri - ver oh down the ri - ver we go.

2 m m m m m m f f f f r r r r r r m m m m

Vi - va la vi - va la vi - va l'a - mour, vi - va la vi - va la vi - va l'a - mour.

d d d d d d r r r r t, t, t, l, t, d

Vi - va la vi - va la vi - va l'a - mour, vi - va la com - pa - nie!

Teaching Tips

- Accessible 6/8 material is always useful. Patsch or clap the pulse throughout to feel the ♩ ♪ and ♫ rhythms against the ♩. beat.

- Taught by rote, this song is easy to memorise, and very good for introducing *f* and *t* unconsciously when moving from pentatonic to diatonic material.

- At a later stage, work with stick notation to help reinforce *f* and *t*.

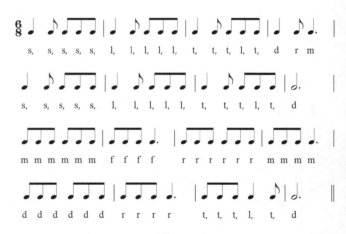

- The selection of notes used in this song is extremely helpful as preparation for the sight-singing in AB aural tests (Grade 4 and 5). After learning the solfa, sing on the letter names in the specified keys.

Way Down Yonder in the Cornfields

The opening of this likeable song has some resemblance to *Old Macdonald Had a Farm*, so make sure the melodies are learned correctly with solfa.

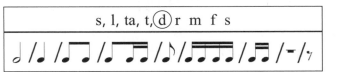

Traditional

Teaching Tips

- Before singing, clap the middle section as a two-part exercise (echo rhythms).

- This arrangement is good for reinforcing *f* and *t*, and for inner-hearing tonic and dominant seventh harmonies (chords I and V7).

- The word rhythms give lots of material for work on semiquaver patterns ▯▯▯▯ (*tiri tiri*) and ▯▯▯ (*te tiri*).

Walk Along Joe

Pentatonic material lends itself to adding ostinatos, and an effective and simple way to make a two-part arrangement is to divide a song between two groups and add an ostinato accompaniment to each section.

American traditional, arranged by Erzsébet Szönyi

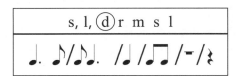

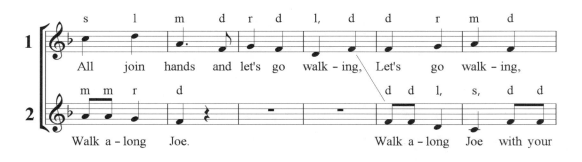

Teaching Tips

- This is ideal material for "dictating" on hand signs: present it in this way phrase by phrase and get the children to sing it back in solfa.

- Make sure the whole group knows the complete song before you add the parts.

- Make up a different arrangement – try other ostinato motifs suggested by the song:

- If the idea of a "paper collar" seems a little old-fashioned, the children could come up with some modern alternatives! eg, Leather jacket.

Hey Dum Bar de Ay (Rainforest Song)

Try this with a large group of children or adults. Teach it by rote, and get into the spirit of improvisation.

African Chant

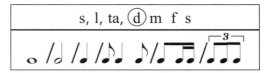

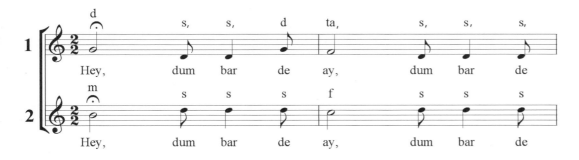

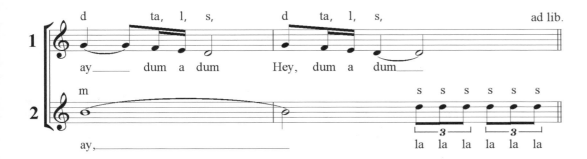

Suggested Performance

All open by softly tapping two fingers on hand to simulate raindrops.

Start group 1 *pianissimo*. Repeat with small *crescendo*, and fade out raindrops.

Start group 2. Repeat ad lib as both groups make a *crescendo*.

Make gradual *diminuendo* to *piano*.

End with raindrops in unison with group 1 and, finally, raindrops alone.

Teaching Tips

- It is quite difficult to pitch the F♮ (*ta*) accurately at first, so make sure this is secure before putting the parts together. The result is a beautiful two-part harmony where *ta* is experienced and enjoyed unconsciously.

- Try singing this on alternative solfa with G = *s*. This clarifies the Mixolydian scale (centred on *s*).

Wo-ye-le

The canoe paddlers on Lake Tanganyika chant to help them work together in rhythm. One of their chants inspired this two-voice musical impression.

Words and music by Josef Marais, based on a traditional chant

Teaching Tips

■ Add this rhythmic ostinato throughout: ♩ ♪♪ ♪

■ The rhythm is very different, but it is interesting to compare the tone set of this song with the well known Canadian *Canoe Song* (no 19: *Flying a Round*: A & C Black 1982).

Fire Down Below

Traditional

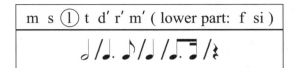

2   Oh, there's fire on the main deck, there's fire on the poop,
    To my way hay ee i oh!
    Oh, there's fire in the galley a-burning up the soup
    There's fire down below!

3   Oh, there's fire in the capstan, there's fire in the hatch
    To my way hay ee i oh!
    Oh there's fire in my whiskers, I needn't strike a match,
    There's fire down below!

Teaching Tips

■   The melody is in the natural minor or Aeolian Mode (*l, t, d r m f s l*), but the lower part introduces *si,* the sharpened seventh, providing a good opportunity for learning to tune both *s* and *si*. This is a useful exercise for young string players as well as vocalists.

■   See the introduction to the section on *Songs in the Minor* (page 46) for a fuller explanation of minor tonality.

33

5 Action Songs

Doing something whilst singing is probably as old an activity as singing itself. Accompanying a song or rhyme with an action reinforces the awareness of pulse, and provides a powerful aid to the memory. When the action is a game or a dance, a child's appetite for repetition is insatiable. In repeating the game over and over again a child will absorb, deep into a subconscious level, the melodic and rhythmic patterns that occur in the song. This forms an essential stage in the learning process prior to looking at and reading the written symbol.

Action songs are above all lots of fun, and here are some favourites, all tried and tested.

Rhythm Canon

Avon Gillespie

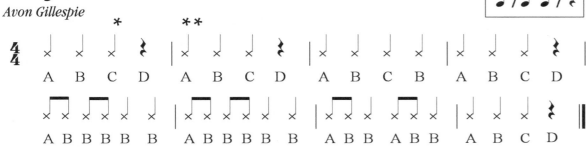

Key to actions

A: Knee slap (patsch)

B: Clap

C: Finger click

D: Clear, but pitchless, outbreath "ha" with open hand gesture

* & ** Two possible canon entries

Rhythm Machine

Heard by Douglas Scarfe, from Musicianship Course by Fiona Gaffney

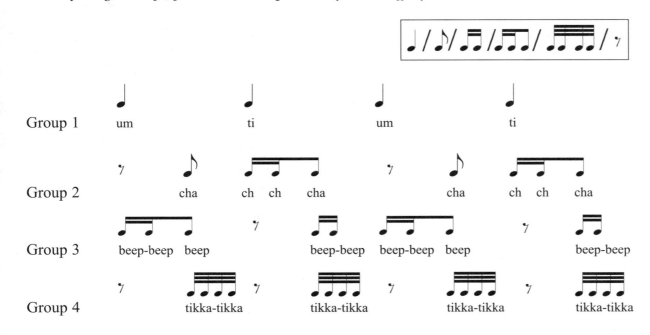

Teaching Tips

- The words "keep it very steady" (bars 5/6) and "little ones, little ones" (bar 7) may be used to help with rhythm.

- Wonderful for physical and mental co-ordination, concentration, and focusing a group at the beginning of a lesson.

- Try adding solfa as follows, using the given rhythm:

  d m s   d m s   d m s m   d m s

  d r m f s l   d r m f s l   d r m d r m   d m s

Instructions

- Divide the class into four groups.

- Make sure each group can manage their part before combining the parts.

Teaching Tips

- Good for large groups.

- Vary pitch of the different parts.

- Smaller groups could transfer the parts to instruments.

- Add suitable actions depicting the workings of a machine.

- Make up a series of sounds and actions for your own machine!

Bim Bam

Traditional Yiddish circle dance

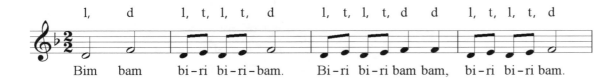

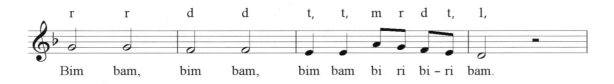

Dance Instructions

First Practise these dance steps individually:

1. Step sideways with R foot.

2. Place L foot behind R, weight on ball of foot.

3. Step sideways on R foot.

4. Place L foot in front of R, weight on ball of foot.

5. & 6. Repeat 1. & 2.

7. Step sideways on R foot.

8. Swing L foot forward (point toe – do not put weight on it) ready to step L for next 8 beats.

Next Form a circle with arms on the shoulders of both neighbours. Circle R for 8 beats, then L, using the dance steps. Then combine with the song!

START SLOWLY then get faster.

Teaching Tips

■ Once the song is learned, it can be accompanied with a simple vocal or instrumental ostinato on an open fifth:

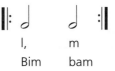

■ Talk about *accelerando*.

Mr Scarfe's Action Round

Douglas Scarfe, from Musicianship Course by Fiona Gaffney

Teaching Tips

- Learn the actions first.

- Starting at a slow, steady pace, sing the theme.

- Sing theme and add actions one by one. Ensure each one is secure before adding the next.

- Sing in canon.

BEATS	1	2	3	4	
ACTIONS					
1 (step)	R foot	L foot	R foot	L foot ‖	Keep going
2	♩ clap	𝄽	𝄽	𝄽 ‖	
3	♩ clap	♫ L R (chest)	𝄽	𝄽 ‖	
4	♩ clap	♫ L R (chest)	♩ slap L leg	♩ slap R leg ‖	Keep going

37

Hi Lo Chickalo

Collected by Frances Middleton (aged 13).
Playground singing game, Ashford C. of E. School, Middlesex

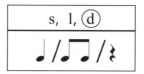

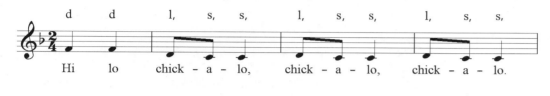

d   d   l,   s,   s,   l,   s,   s,   l,   s,   s,

Hi   lo   chick – a – lo,   chick – a – lo,   chick – a – lo.

d   d   l,   s,   s,   l,   s,   s,   d

Hi   lo   chick – a – lo,   chick – a – lo,   Hi!

Playing the Game

■ Children face their partner, and each child holds hands palms together with fingers pointing forward towards partner.

■ Each child's left hand is back to back with partner's left hand.

■ Only the right hand moves.

■ On the word "Hi", clap right hands together above left hands.

■ On the word "lo", clap right hands together below left hands.

■ On "chick" clap own left hand.

■ There is a clap for every beat.

Teaching Tips

■ Very useful for reinforcing the *d l, s,* tone set.

■ If the children start in a circle, at the end of the game they can swing round and play again with another partner.

Oncorrianda

Collected by Sarah Middleton (aged 10).
Playground singing game, Ashford C. of E. School, Middlesex

On - cor - ri - an - da said to me, on my

way, on my way like an A B C

SPOKEN

Sen - na Sen - na Woo - ster Sea, Sen - na Sen - na Woo - ster Sea Un, deux, trois!

Playing the Game

■ A circle of children sit with their hands turned palms up.

■ All *right* hands are on top of neighbours' *left* hands, ie. all *left* hands are underneath neighbours' *right* hands.

■ The Leader (initially the teacher) swings *right* hand across to clap the right hand of the child on his/her left. The Leader's hand then returns to starting position.

■ This movement is passed clockwise around the circle from child to child, with one clap to each beat.

■ The action continues through the final chant at the same speed. The child whose hand is clapped on "trois" is out.

Teaching Tips

■ Very good song for *fa*.

■ Make sure the children have clapped the ♩ pulse and walked the beat as they sing, before they try the game actions.

■ Ultimately you can play this, not as an elimination game, but with the last child becoming a new Leader. But beware trying this too soon! The Leader needs to have pulse, pitch and action all integrated in "inner thinking" in order to start the game successfully, which requires concentration, confidence and co-ordination.

■ Try playing the game anti-clockwise instead of clockwise for a change. (Hands will need to be arranged the other way round at the start).

Kapa (The Cat)

Ugandan circle game. With thanks to Bob Walker

Pronunciation Guide

Kah pah! Ay go bah go bah,
Kah pah! Ay go bah may say.

Translation

The cat is chasing the rat.

Playing the Game

■ All form a circle holding hands.

■ Two children are chosen, one to be the rat, inside the circle, and one to be the cat, who is outside.

■ The cat must try and catch the rat by pursuing it in and out of the arches formed by the raised arms of the group, who help the rat but try and stop the cat, while everyone sings the song.

■ When the rat is finally caught, the two players forming the last arch it passed through become the new contestants.

Teaching Tips

■ Good for quaver upbeat, which can be reinforced by a drum playing the rhythm sung by the Leader:

Ka - pa!

Dipidu

Ugandan traditional

Good day, good day to you. Good day, O dip-i-du.

Dip dip dip dip di-pi-du, di-pi-du O di-pi-du.

This is a useful song for working in stick notation.

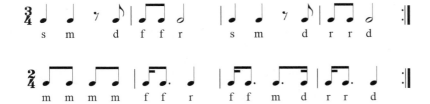

Teaching Tips

- A good example of changing metre, which could be reinforced by facing a partner and doing the following actions on each beat:

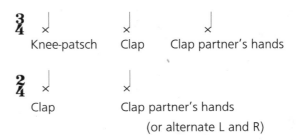

- Get the children to try out ostinatos for chime bars or xylophone, using *d* and *s*:

	LH	RH	RH			LH	RH
3/4	s,	s	s		**2/4**	s,	s
or:	d	d'	d'		or:	d	d'
or:	d	s	s		or:	d	s

Ding Dong

American singing game

Ding dong! I've got a rhy-thm in my head! Hot dog! I've

got a rhy-thm in my head! Ding dong! I've

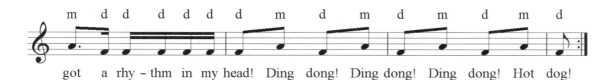

got a rhy-thm in my head! Ding dong! Ding dong! Ding dong! Hot dog!

Playing the Game

Partners stand facing one another

Ding dong	*Pat partner's shoulders twice*
I've got a rhythm in my head	
Hot dog	*Stamp feet twice*
I've got a rhythm in my head	
Ding dong	*Pat partner's shoulders*
I've got a rhythm in my head	
Ding dong	*Clap, then clap partner's RH*
Ding dong	*Clap, then clap partner's LH*
Ding dong	*Clap, then patsch on both partner's hands*
Hot dog	*Clap and stamp feet twice*

Teaching Tips

■ Before trying the action game, get the children to clap and count all the "*Ding dongs*" as you sing. Then add a different action, eg knee patsch, on the "*Hot dogs*".

■ Practise and learn the actions for the last two bars before attempting the whole song.

■ Get faster as you get into the swing.

Duck Dance

American Indian

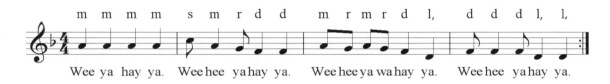

m m m m s m r d d m r m r d l, d d d l, l,

Wee ya hay ya. Wee hee yahay ya. Wee hee ya wa hay ya. Wee hee yahay ya.

m r m r d l, d d d l, l, m m m m

Wee hee ya wa hay ya. Wee hee ya hay ya. Ho ke lay ho!

Teaching Tips

■ A song of great rhythmic energy. Children could improvise their own circle dances once the song has been well-learned.

■ Try singing it in canon with successive entries at half a bar or whole bar distance.

■ Add a part in augmentation (ie. at half speed) during the first line.

■ Lots of use can be made of ostinatos, both rhythmic and melodic, from a very simple ♩ (*ta-a*) drum-beat throughout, to more complicated motifs, some of which the children can find for themselves in the song. Try the ones below on a drum, or with voice or instrument.

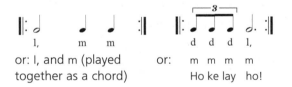

l, m m

or: l, and m (played together as a chord)

d d d l,

or: m m m m

Ho ke lay ho!

■ The following rhythmic ostinatos are more complicated but, once mastered, the children could make up their own melodies, using notes of the pentatonic scale.

tri-o-la ta-a te te

tri-o-la ta syn-co-pa

Love Grows Under

Girl Guide singing game

Teaching Tips

■ The idea is to start at quite a leisurely speed for the first time through. Then increase the speed on the second and again on the third (and last!) repetition. The actions need to be secure before you can speed up.

Everyone sits in a circle and does the actions together. The action sequence is repeated four times as the song is sung.
The pictures are drawn as if you were looking at yourself in a mirror.

As I Was Walking

Traditional

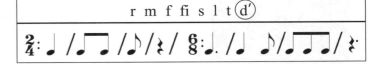

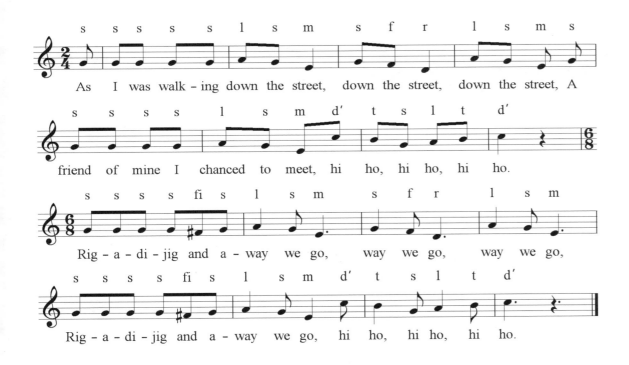

As I was walk-ing down the street, down the street, down the street, A
friend of mine I chanced to meet, hi ho, hi ho, hi ho.
Rig-a-di-jig and a-way we go, way we go, way we go,
Rig-a-di-jig and a-way we go, hi ho, hi ho, hi ho.

Dance Instructions

■ The children form two facing rows about 2 metres apart, each child facing a partner (Long-ways set formation).

■ The top of the set is the end nearest the music or caller.

■ If there are a lot of children, make several sets with an average of five couples per set.

– Bars 1–2   Four steps forward on the beat.

– Bars 3–4   Four steps back on the beat.

– Bars 5–8   Holding partner's hands, turn a clockwise circle and return to place.

– Bars 9–12   Top couple take a two-hand hold and gallop down the middle to the bottom.

– Bars 13–16 All partners hold cross hands, and swing, returning to place in time for repeat of the dance.

■ With each repeat there is a new top couple.

Teaching Tips

■ This song is a lovely combination of simple and compound time. The dance helps the children to feel the difference in a very natural way.

■ For another dance with changing metre, try the Danish dance, *Swedish Masquerade*. Contact the Society for International Folk Dancing for the dance instructions and advice on the music. Current information on the SIFD is kept by the English Folk Dance and Song Society at Cecil Sharp House, 2 Regents Park Road, London.

6 | Songs in the Minor

The best way to introduce minor tonality is to start with simple songs using the *la* pentatonic scale (*l, d r m s l*), the *la* pentachord (*l, t, d r m*), and the natural minor or Aeolian mode (*l, t, d r m f s l*). There are many good *la* centred songs with a limited tone set, which can be easily taught by rote before the concept of minor is made conscious. (See *Duck Dance*, *Che Che Kule*, *Bim Bam*, *Step Back Baby* and *Chicka Hanka* for good examples elsewhere in this book).

The main difficulty with minor tonality is the chromatic alterations, mainly to the sixth and seventh notes of the scale, which can present some confusions and some tuning difficulties. But if foundation work has been laid with the natural minor scale, the change from *f* to *fi* (sharpened sixth) and *s* to *si* (sharpened seventh) is both easier to tune and easier to understand on paper. Here are the three most common forms of the *la* minor scale.

- Natural minor   l, t, d r m f s l

- Harmonic minor   l, t, d r m f *si* l

- Melodic minor   l, t, d r m *fi si* l (ascending)

                                 l *s f* m r d t, l, (descending)

Minor keys are often associated with sadness, and indeed many of our finest folk songs use minor modes to express sorrow, mourning and loss. But this is not always the case, and you will find in this section and elsewhere songs in minor tonality with very different moods. Children often find minor songs very appealing, and once they are conscious of *la* tonality as opposed to *do* tonality, they will enjoy compositions and improvisations centred on *la*.

Farewell

Fiona Gaffney's words express the mood of sadness often conveyed by minor tonality in this haunting folk-song.

Hungarian folk-song, words by Fiona Gaffney

Teaching Tips

■ This is a useful song for working on the *la* pentachord (*l, t, d r m*).

■ Young pianists will be able to manage this once they have mastered a five-finger position. More advanced pianists may like to try Bartók's challenging arrangement of about Grade 3–4 standard (*Round Dance*, from *For Children*, Vol. I, Boosey & Hawkes, 1947).

Mosquito Song

This solfa exercise sounds like the insistent whining of mosquitos when it is sung fast and lightly in canon. Like the last song, it uses only the first five notes of the minor scale (*la* pentachord). With its easy stepwise melody it is quickly learned. We present it here in stick notation. Teach by rote, using hand signs to help.

Hungarian dance song

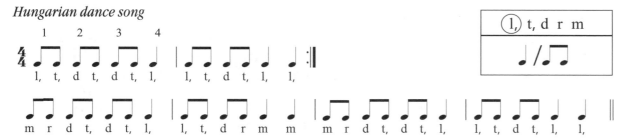

Teaching Tips

■ Start simply: sing it in two parts before you try four.

■ Keyboard players can rise to the challenge of playing this in two parts (hands an octave apart), or trying it in four parts with a friend. Start them in A or D minor, then let them explore other white key starting positions to discover which black keys they need in each position to create the sound of the *la* pentachord.

■ It's fun to use a simple canon such as this as a warm-up for a small group of string or wind players. It requires a lot of concentration to keep good ensemble in four parts!

Rumanian Canon

Anon., words by Celia Waterhouse

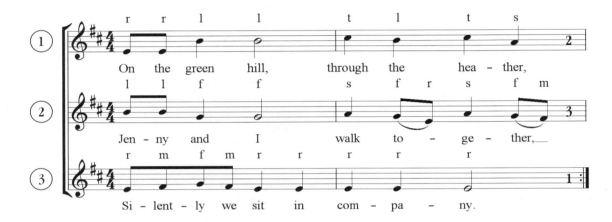

Rise Up, O Flame

This beautiful canon is harder than the three preceding songs because of its more complex rhythms and melodic jumps.

Michael Praetorius

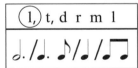

Teaching Tips

- This lovely tune is in the Dorian mode (centred on *re*). The Dorian scale is introduced from Grade 1 in the new AB Jazz syllabus.

  Dorian mode   r m f s l t d' r'

Many British folk-songs use this tonality. You can find one of them on page 98 (*The Diamond*).

- Well-known songs in Dorian mode:
  - *Noel Nouvelet* (French carol) and its English counterpart, the Easter hymn *Now the Green Blade Riseth*
  - *God is Love* (hymn)
  - *What Shall We Do With a Drunken Sailor?*
  - *Scarborough Fair*.

Teaching Tips

- Work on getting good tuning in the rising fifth (*l,–m*) and falling fourth (*l–m*).

- A useful song for feeling the full length of ♩. It's helpful to try the canon clapped on rhythm only before singing it.

- For perfect ensemble in the canon, get everyone to tap the first beat of each bar as they sing it the first few times.

48

"A" Melodic Minor Song

Instrumental teachers usually favour the harmonic minor scale for practical exams up to Grade 5, but the melodic minor is introduced in the AB theory syllabus from Grade 2 onwards. Solfa is a wonderful aid for learning all forms of the minor, since it makes the chromatic alterations (*fi* and *si*) so easy to understand. You can find the three most common forms of the *la* minor scale presented in solfa in the introduction to this section on page 46. The melodic minor is especially beautiful to sing.

Words and music by Fiona Gaffney from Musicianship Course

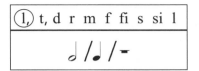

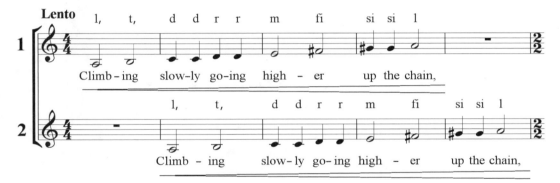

Teaching tips

■ Make sure the children have sung songs and scales in the natural minor before trying this song.

Heidi

Danish Girl Guide song

Teaching Tips

- The ♩♫ (*te tiri*) rhythm can be experienced unconsciously with this song. Clap bar 2 several times and say the words.

- There is a lot of energy in the rest because of its unresolved harmony. Add a stamp or clap here.

- Simple movement sequence:
  - Deep sidestep L and close three times (three bars).
  - On third close, keep weight on L foot and clap on the rest.
  - fourth bar – sway R–L.
  - Repeat melody and perform the same sequence starting R.
  - Repeat same sequence L then R for second part of melody.

- Once mastered, the children can perform this sequence in two facing parallel lines or concentric circles. Decide which line or circle is going to begin (group 1). When group 2 starts, the lines will be moving in opposite directions.

Vem Kan Segla Förutan Vind?

Swedish pronunciation is, for the most part, phonetic. A lot of the vowels are long.

Swedish folk-song

1. Vem kan seg-la för-u-tan vind? Vem kan ro u-tan å-ror?
   fur - oo - taan   *oo - taan oar - er*
2. Jag kan seg-la för-u-tan vind. Jag kan ro u-tan å-ror.
   Yaag

Vem kan skil-jas från vän-nen sin u-tan at fäl-la tå-ror?
fwee - yaas fron ven - nen   *fel - la taw - rer*
Men ej skil-jas från vän-nen min u-tan at fäl-la tå-ror.
eh fwee - yaas

Translation

1 Who can sail without wind?
Who can row without oars?
Who can part from their beloved
without shedding tears?

2 I can sail without wind.
I can row without oars.
But I can't part from my beloved
without shedding tears.

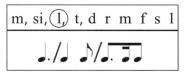

Teaching Tips

■ There are some useful ⁶₈ rhythms in this song. Try some of them as ostinatos,

eg.

■ The song works in canon. Start the second voice when the first voice reaches bar 3.

Sleigh Song

Minor does not always convey a mood of sadness, as this rhythmic Russian song ably demonstrates.

Russian folk-song. English translation by Geoffrey Brace

Teaching Tips

- Lightly-strummed guitar chords add to the trotting effect, as well as lots of sleigh bells for the troika.

- Useful for ♩. ♪ rhythms.

- Teach the main melody first. The lower part is easy to pick up as it shadows the main tune.

2 Loud we hear the harness jingle,
   And the driver sings a song.
   Eyes a-flame and cheeks a-tingle,
   Merrily we race along.

   Chorus
   Singing, singing, singing, sleigh-bells ringing,
   Merrily we race along.

Rainbow Girl

Folk-song from Suiyuan, Northern China

```
      l   s m l   s m  l l  s l        l   s m l  s m  r r   d r
Hoong tsai_may  may_ en ai hai yo   Chang der_how na mo  en ai  hai yo

      m   m s l  d' l  s   m m  s d      m  m   m  m m  l, l,  s, l,
Ying tao_  shiaow_ koa_  en ai  hai yo  Yir dien dien na mo  en ai  hai yo
```

Pronunciation Guide

Hoong chai may may	yee-a high-oh!
as in Chinese	
Chang de how na mo	yee-a high-oh!
Ying tao chiauw ko	yee-a high-oh!
Yi den den na mo	yee-a high-oh!

Translation

My sweetheart is like the rainbow:
oh how wholesome is her glow!
Her little mouth is like a red berry:
oh how exquisitely tiny it is!

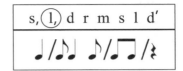

```
s, (l,) d r m s l d'
```

Teaching Tips

■ Although it has quite a wide range, the rhythmic and melodic repetitions make this song easy to learn.

■ A good song for the ♪♪ ♪ (*syncopa*) rhythm. As you sing the song, get the children to put up their hands every time they hear this rhythm. Use bar 2 as a rhythmic or melodic ostinato throughout.

■ Try it also in augmentation:

is a strong rhythmic accompaniment.

■ The song works as a canon at the second bar.

■ For a Chinese effect, add a cymbal crash in the rest.

53

Bird of Heaven

In his introduction to his songbook *In the Present Tense,* Sydney Carter says: "There is no correct way of doing any of these songs, only ways that work or do not work. A song is a device for making something happen. If it happens, it will not matter how you did it". We offer his song here with the same invitation.

Words and music by Sydney Carter, arranged by Celia Waterhouse. Copyright 1969 Stainer & Bell Ltd, London, England. Quotation from 'In the Present Tense' (published by Stainer & Bell)

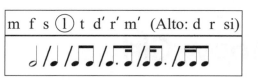

Teaching Tips

- Try this lovely song unaccompanied, or with the suggested chords played on guitar, keyboard or folk harp. The lower part can be sung, or played on a mellow instrument such as a treble recorder.

2 Lock him in religion
Gold and frankincense and myrrh
Carry to his prison,
But he will be gone.

Chorus

3 Temple made of marble
Beak and feather made of gold.
All the bells are ringing,
But the bird has gone.

Chorus

4 Bell and book and candle
Cannot hold him any more,
For the bird is flying
As he did before.

Chorus
(Last time)
Ah! the bird of heaven!
Follow where the bird has gone;
If you want to find him,
Keep on travelling on.

- Vary the arrangement with a solo voice for some of the verses.

- The song contains some unusual rhythms, but the words of verse 1 are helpful for learning them.

- Guitarists might find the chords easier to play in E minor. The children can work out the new chord pattern for themselves as a transposition exercise. Every chord needs to be transposed down a minor third (ie. Gm > Em, D7 > B7, etc). If you still want to sing the song in G minor, use a capo on the third fret to bring the pitch up a minor third again.

7 Quodlibets

"As You Please" Songs

Quodlibets – otherwise known as partner songs or mix-and-match songs – are great fun to sing and have a good deal of learning value. Even the putting together of two simple songs that have each been known and enjoyed for a long time makes for a surprising challenge. Quodlibets give an instant feeling of fuller orchestration, and the exciting rhythmic and harmonic combinations bring a real sense of achievement.

Many pentatonic songs can be successfully fitted together. In other material you can discover potential quodlibet partners by analysing the chord pattern of songs to find matching harmonies. Then look for similar tempo, metre and phrase length. Songs that are too similar in melody, on the other hand, don't work well together.

To teach quodlibets, first make sure that the individual songs have been taught previously and are secure. Most of the songs in this section have teaching tips for working on each song by itself before putting it together with its partner. Successful combination of the songs depends on how well the children have internalised the basic pulse with each one. Lots of clapping or walking the pulse is as usual an essential foundation.

Make sure that you are confident in cueing in the two songs. This means not only giving the two starting pitches (solfa is of course a great aid here) but also, if it is a staggered start, that you know exactly where to start one song in relation to the other. It's sometimes easier, and indeed more effective in performance, if one (or both) groups sing their song through once before coming in together.

Here's a way to check how well you *really* know the partner songs in combination yourself! Can you sing one and clap the rhythm of the other while you walk the beat? Any conductor worth his/her salt should be able to do this as a matter of course!

7

Step Back Baby / Chicka Hanka

5 Should've seen the way those robbers ran.
6 I picked up my frying pan.

7 Some flew east and some flew west.
8 Some flew over the cuckoo's nest.

Step Back Baby

American Singing Game

The song has a limited tone set centred around *la*.
Children enjoy its jazzy mood and catchy words.

Teaching Tips

■ Use it to help young voices to develop by dividing the lines between different groups or soloists

■ Make the ⸙ rest conscious by taking it in turns to step back and clap on this beat.

■ Use the word rhythms to help you teach

(*tiri tiri*)   (*te tiri*) and   (*tiri te*).

Chicka Hanka

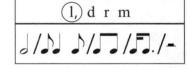

American Singing Game

Teaching Tips

■ A good song for introducing *la* tonality.

■ Use it to reinforce the ♪♩ ♪ (*syncopa*) rhythm.

■ Choose a small group to make a rhythmic accompaniment with whispered chanting through all the minims and ━ rests:

Chicka Hanka

This gives the impression of a chuffing steam train.

Rockin' by the Baby / My Owlet

These two American lullabies are both useful for their catchy rhythms, and for practising *dolce* and *piano* singing.

Rockin' by the Baby

American traditional

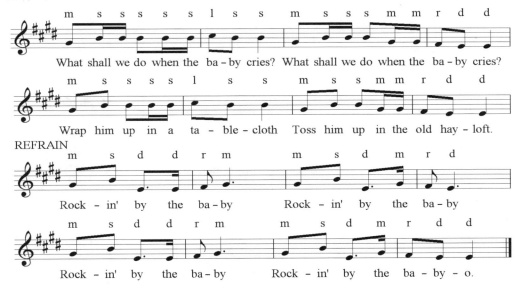

What shall we do when the ba – by cries? What shall we do when the ba – by cries?

Wrap him up in a ta – ble – cloth Toss him up in the old hay – loft.

REFRAIN

Rock – in' by the ba – by Rock – in' by the ba – by

Rock – in' by the ba – by Rock – in' by the ba – by – o.

My Owlet (*A round*)

Kiowa Indian lullaby

① Ow – let, my ow – let is sleep – ing,

② Wee stars are twink – ling in the sky,

Mo – ther is sing – ing lul la – by.

Teaching Tips

- Useful for the [te tiri] (*te tiri*) and [temri] (*temri*) rhythms, as well as the more unusual [te ta-e] (*te ta-e*).
- For simple and effective ostinato try:

  r d d
  Baby - o

Make sure the children take a breath every four bars!

- A longer ostinato is:

  m s d d r m
  Rock-in' by the ba - by

Performance Suggestion for the Quodlibet

Divide the class into three groups. Each group sings their song twice through.

Group 1   Start *Rockin'*

Group 2   Start *Owlet* when Group 1 reaches Refrain.

Group 3   Start *Owlet* in canon when Group 1 start their repeat. Song ends with Group 3 singing their last line alone.

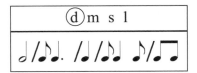

Teaching Tips

- Make a simple accompaniment with:

  Lul - la - by

either sung or played as an ostinato by three different voices or chimebars, each one gently repeating a different note of the *do* chord (*d m* or *s*).

Seagull Sit on the Shore /
London Bridge is Falling Down

Two simple traditional songs can combine to make an exciting performance.

2   Penguin, penguin, swim in the sea
3   Puffin, puffin, fly in the sky

Be your Own Quodlibet Arranger

These songs both follow the same chord pattern (I, I, V7, I). Many other songs share the same harmonies, and with a bit of experience you can learn which ones fit well together. Here is a selection, most of which can be found in *Flying a Round* (A & C Black, 1982):

- A Ram Sam Sam (or its modern equivalent, A Pizza Hut)

- Old Woman, Old Woman

- Pease Porridge Hot

- Alouette

- Down in Demerara

- Alabama Gal (see page 3)

Try out any of them in combination to discover which ones make the best music. You need to think carefully about the tempo: *Pease Porridge* and *Alouette* need to be at half speed to work together with some of the others.

Seagull Sit on the Shore

Traditional

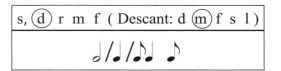

Teaching Tips

- Another useful song for ♪ ♩ ♪ (*syncopa*)

- The descant is easy to pick up as it shadows the melody. Complete the harmony with a third voice following the chord pattern:

    o   o   o   o
    d   d   s, d

- Once this basic harmony is mastered, you can add rhythmic interest on each note:

    ♩   ♩   ♪ ♩ ♪ ♩
    sea - gull   or   sit on the shore

Use the words and rhythms of the song in the last two bars, keeping to the *s,* and *d* pitches.

This third part clarifies the tonic and dominant harmony (chords I and V) and paves the way for recognising perfect cadences (AB Grade 6 Aural Tests).

London Bridge is Falling Down

Traditional

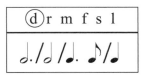

Teaching Tips

- Young children often learn this song at nursery or infant stage, but in this arrangement it is useful with older children for working on the ♩. ♪ rhythm. This is made particularly clear when combined with the crotchet rhythm of *Seagull* in the quodlibet.

- The song is more usually notated in 2/4 time, in notes of half the value,

    ie.

    2/4 ♩. ♪ ♪ ♩ | ♪ ♩ ♩ | etc.
        tem - ri te - te   te - te ta

As a written exercise, ask the children to write this rhythm out using stick notation.

Li'l Liza Jane / Turn the Glasses Over

These two pentatonic songs are both very well known, but they are so versatile that we cannot resist including them as a partnership in this section. Both work individually as rounds, or with one voice singing in augmentation (ie, at half-speed). Both lend themselves to adding ostinato motifs as accompaniment. Combining them as a quodlibet, whether in their simplest form or with any of the above complexities, adds a whole new dimension of fun.

Turn the Glasses Over

Virginian folk-song

Simple Circle Dance

Form a circle with pairs of children holding cross-hands facing anti-clockwise for promenade (i).

1st & 2nd lines	Partners walk around circle for eight ♩ beats.
3rd line	Facing partner and holding hands, swing arms right round overhead (at least twice if possible).
4th line	Mime drinking from a glass and turning glass over.
5th–8th lines	Each child turns to R and begins to walk (in opposite direction from partner, passing by the L shoulder) around the edge of their own circle (ii), to find a new partner ready to start again.

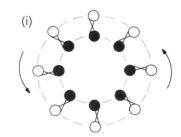

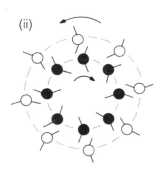

Li'l Liza Jane

American folk-song

2 Liza Jane looks good to me   *Li'l Liza Jane*
    Sweetest one I ever see   "   *Chorus*

3 Where she lives the posies grow   "
    Chickens round the kitchen go   "   *Chorus*

4 What do I care how far we roam?   "
    Where she's at is home sweet home   "   *Chorus*

Teaching Tips

- A good song for reinforcing many semiquaver rhythms:

  (te tiri)   (tiri tiri)   and   (tiri te)

- Useful for *d l*, *s*, as well as notes of the *do* chord (*d m s*).

- Melodic ostinatos from the song:

  d   d   d   l,   s,   d   d   d   l,   s,
  I've been to Har–lem, I've been to Do–ver

  and   m   s   s   m   s   s
  Sail–ing east, Sail–ing west

Teaching Tips

- A very good song for teaching ♪♪ ♩ ♪ (*syncopa*)

  and ♩. ♪. It's also a very clear example of *d'*.

- Melodic ostinatos from the song:

  l   s   m   s   m   m   r   d
  Li'l Li - za Jane   and   Li'l Li - za Jane

You can also build up an exciting accompaniment with all of these motifs together:

d   s,   l,   m   m   f   s   s   l
Jane, Li - za   Jane, Li - za   Jane, Li - za

All Things Shall Perish / Bravo Bravo

Bravo, Bravo

Traditional

s, l, t, ⓓ r m f
♩./♩ ♩/♩. ♪/♩

Teaching Tips

■ Very good for ♩ ♩ and ♩. ♪ ♩ in ¾ time

■ Try as a two-part round, bringing in the second voice halfway through. (The voices will sing the same for the last two bars).

■ Here is a simple movement sequence to go with the song. Take one step to each bar. Each line starts with the R foot first.

> 1st line   Four steps forward.
>
> 2nd line   Four steps back.
>
> 3rd line   Sidestep R and close L to R without
>   transferring weight. Repeat to L.
>
> 4th line   Repeat third line.

When the children have mastered this, try it as a round, forming up the two groups in two facing lines about two metres apart.

This slow step is good training for counting fully through a long note in instrumental practice – usually a very hard skill for children to master.

All Things Shall Perish

German folk-song

s, l, t, ⓓ r m f s l
♩./♩. ♪/♩

Teaching Tips

■ To make the songs work as a quodlibet, the first line has been repeated. In the original version where the first line is sung only once, this song works as a two-part canon with the second voice starting at the fifth bar.

Designing Your Own Chordal Ostinato Accompaniment

The chord pattern of both these songs is I–II–V7–I. As an exercise in harmony, the children can choose one note from each chord to create their own line of accompaniment:

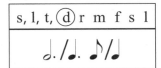

I	II	V7	I
♩.	♩.	♩.	♩.
s	l	f	s
m	f	r	m
d	r	t,	d
		s,	

eg,	m	r	t,	d

Putting a few of these lines together creates a new chordal accompaniment, which can be sung or played to accompany either of the songs individually, or the complete quodlibet.

Hurry Hurry / No Need to Hurry

Traditional Calypso

† *No r' in Hurry Hurry*

Teaching Tips

■ These songs both have a very Caribbean feel, and are typically good for ♪ ♩ ♪ (*syncopa*)

■ It's fun for children to get the hang of the Latin American "calypso" rhythm with these songs. An easy way to start is to add this tapping pattern for both hands, *slowly* at first. It's useful to count quavers to begin with:

When they are good at tapping this as they sing, it's easy to extract the accented beats:

Clap first, then play on claves or woodblock. On the last bar, clap/tap the three accented crotchets:

Hurry Hurry

2   Get along, you sleepy-head, and come on the run
    Must you be so slow and lazy? Day is begun!
    If you do not finish with the work to be done,
    You can't go out and play and have some fun.

No Need to Hurry

2   Don't be so noisy, my little one
    You'll wake the town before you are done.
    If I should work hard out in the sun
    I'll be so tired that I'll have no fun.

8 Harder Part Songs, Rounds & Canons

This second group of rounds, canons and part songs is more ambitious. Let the children first try the easier material which can be found in earlier sections of this book, in order to become accustomed to developing two-part listening skills and true intonation.

All these songs lend themselves to performance. Aim to perform regularly from memory. Any choir will perform better, and connect more with the audience, by keeping eye-contact with their conductor, and the confidence you will build in the children will pay dividends. Obviously with part songs this presents more of a challenge, but after all, a well-developed memory is one of a musician's greatest assets, as well as an asset to learning in any field. As before, use of solfa brings secure learning of parts. Try it and you will discover for yourself.

Chairs to Mend

This three part catch consists of street cries, which are a part of our folk tradition. It is a great favourite with KS2 and 3 pupils.

William Hayes (1706–1777), Old Street Cries.
With thanks to Boosey & Hawkes

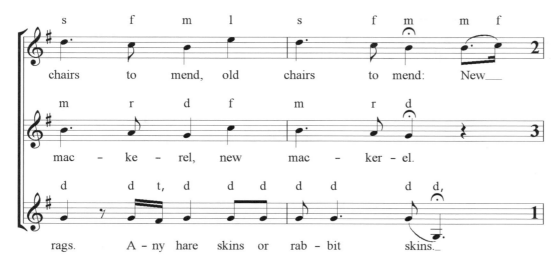

Teaching Tips

■ Useful for teaching dotted rhythms.

■ Use it for cross-curricular work with history or drama, ie. make up your own street cries, dress up and act out a street scene in Victorian times (or modern times, if you prefer!).

■ More examples of street cries can be found in *The Cries of London*, arranged for SATTB and viols by Orlando Gibbons, and "*Who will buy*?" from the musical *Oliver* by Lionel Bart.

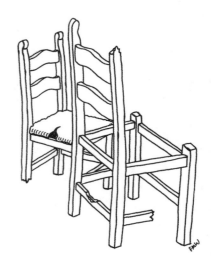

Two Canons by Luigi Cherubini (1760–1842)

Luigi Cherubini, words by Nandita Hollins

These two Cherubini canons reinforce work with the tonic chord and the whole scale. With their underlying tonic and dominant harmonies, they are easy to learn and produce a rich, full sound when sung in three parts.

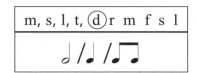

Ha Ha Ha

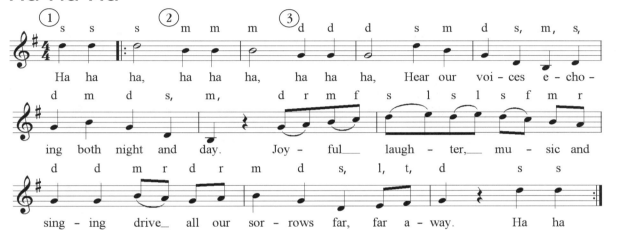

Teaching Tips

■ Use three different voices for the first three bars, each singing three notes and holding the third one until all are singing. In this way, you hear the notes of the major triad chord I (s - m - d) sung separately and sustained as a chord.

■ You can also use parts of this song to practise other elements of the solfa scale:

– s, and m,
– singing the first six notes of the scale (*drmfsl*) quite quickly
– introducing s, l, t, d – a common ending to songs.

In Praise of Solfa

This is particularly useful for introducing teenagers to the fun of solfa singing.

Teaching Tips

■ Teach this song by rote first, singing the words.

■ Then sing it in solfa all the way through. You cover the whole scale and can introduce the sound of the dominant seventh (s, - t, - r - f) and tonic (d - m - s) chords, (V₇ and I).

■ If you are working with older pupils who already read music, get them to read it in solfa from the beginning. They will find it an enjoyable challenge.

67

Janie Mama

This traditional calypso is ideal teaching material for older children

Traditional calypso

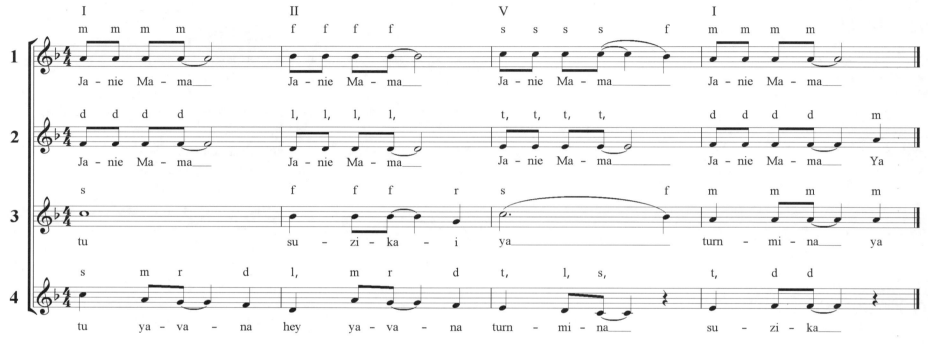

Teaching Tips

■ The I–II–V7–I chord progression on which this song is based, can serve as a good aural foundation for understanding and hearing the harmony required for Grade 5 theory and for work with blues and jazz.

■ The chords are not all in root position, so this gives you a good opportunity to practise singing inversions. (Very useful for AB aural examinations.)

Si Si Si

This lively Congolese song is performed as follows: Section A, Section B, Section C, Section A, Sections B and C together, Section A

Congolese folk-song

Teaching Tips

- Emphasise the dotted minim with three claps or three knee patsches each time it occurs.

- Sway as you sing!

Hashivenu

Sung in slow 3 time, this Hebrew round is a beautiful example of the Aeolian mode, or natural minor (*l, t, d r m f s l*). Pronounced "hasheevaynoo", the words (taken from Lamentations) are translated as "Turn thou us unto thee, O Lord, and we shall be turned; renew our days as of old".

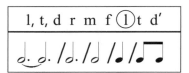

Meir Ben Uri, Lamentations 5:21

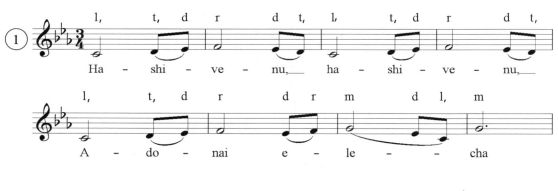

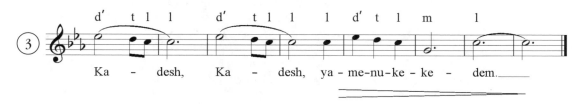

Teaching Tips

■ Use the first line for reinforcing work with the minor tonality (*l,–t,–d–r–m*).

■ There are other useful passages for solfa work, eg: *m–f   m–l   l–t–d'*

but beware of spoiling the enjoyment of the song by too much analysis.

■ It is a useful song for introducing or reinforcing *crescendo* and *diminuendo*.

Liberian chant, collected by Andrew Connor

Ba-nu-wa

This beautiful song from Liberia is a great favourite with anyone who has ever sung it. Because of its improvisatory style, we have not included the rhythms in lines 5 and 8 in the rhythm summary.

Teaching Tips

- Divide the group into nine suitable sections, each to sing one line.

  - Group 1 sings line one twice before adding the other groups in turn.

  - Each group continues to sing only the one line, as the others join in, building up a crescendo of sound.

  - Encourage the children to improvise other parts.

  - When a climax has been reached, each group falls silent – starting with the last and ending with Group 1.

- Boys with broken voices will enjoy singing line 4.

Tzena Tzena

This Israeli folk-song, with its catchy rhythms, may be sung as a three part round to accompany the energetic Israeli circle dance known as the Horra.

Israeli folk-song

① Tze-na tze-na tze-na tze-na, Can't you hear the mu-sic play-ing in___ the ci-ty square?

② Tze - na tze - na Join the ce - le - bra - tion, There'll be peo - ple there from ev - 'ry na - tion.

③ Tze - na tze - na Join the ce - le - bra - tion, There'll be peo - ple dan - cing there.

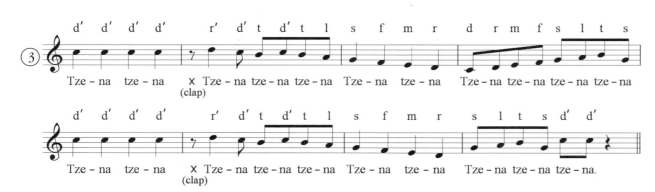

③ Tze-na tze-na x Tze-na tze-na tze-na Tze-na tze-na Tze-na tze-na tze-na tze-na
(clap)

Tze-na tze-na x Tze-na tze-na tze-na Tze-na tze-na Tze-na tze-na tze-na.
(clap)

Teaching Tips

- All link arms or put arms around neighbours' shoulders.

  - Step forward with L foot. R foot cross over behind L. Change direction at each line.

- Useful for teaching:

  - dotted rhythms: ♩. ♪ and ♩. ♪
  - quaver rests, crotchet rests
  - tied notes
  - dotted minims.

The Mountains I Love

This lilting Swiss folk-song is very versatile, as both a part song and a round. It can be accompanied with simple guitar chords or a bass ostinato part.

Swiss folk-song, arranged by Douglas Coombes. English text by John Emlyn Edwards. Arrangement from Lindsay Folk Book, *reproduced with kind permission of Lindsay Music (© Lindsay Music 1980)*

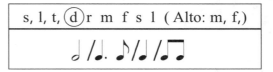

1.Too long I've been a ro-ver, Ne-ver rest-ing, e-ver quest-ing, But

now I'm turn-ing home-ward To the moun-tains I love.

CHORUS

And the moun-tain bird fly-ing, With the sun-light on his wings, Will be

wait-ing to greet me With the bright song that he sings.

Ostinato

Teaching Tips

■ Sing this song in two parts (SA), repeating the chorus between each verse.

■ Try it as a two-part round, the second group starting the verse, when the first group reaches the chorus. When this is secure, try the parts and the round together.

■ Add the given ostinato on a bass instrument, or play the chords on guitar or keyboard.

2 Men praised a mighty city
   So I strayed there, never stayed there,
   No marvel could it show me
   Like the mountains I love.   *Chorus*

3 I've left on distant oceans
   Magic islands, never my lands,
   For none possessed the wonder
   Of the mountains I love.   *Chorus*

4 No more will I go roaming
   Never knowing where I'm going,
   At last I've found the pathway
   To the mountains I love.   *Chorus*

9 Singable Songs

Ever needed an item to fill a gap in a school concert; or wanted to round off a lesson with a song whose main artistic and educational merit lies in its beauty? Then look no further than this collection taken from both sides of the Atlantic. There are songs to cheer, soothe, amuse and, most importantly, enjoy. Exposure to beauty awakens a life-long response to it and provides each growing child with a musical gold standard against which he or she can measure all future musical experiences.

No apologies for the seemingly paradoxical sounding title. Just enjoy.

One ' These Fine Mornings

Spiritual

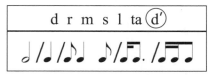

Teaching Tips

■ Teach by rote, paying special attention to the rhythm in the last line, second bar.

■ Works well in canon one bar apart, and creates an interesting effect in augmentation.

■ Use ♪♩ ♪ (*syncopa*) rhythm as a percussive ostinato.

■ Melodic ostinatos which are effective are

■ Perform with alternate solo and chorus lines, or in two groups.

---

2 If you don't ever see me again

I'm going home on a cloud

I'm going to hail the morning train

I'm going home on a cloud.

3 I'm a poor pilgrim travelling alone

I'm going home on a cloud

Gonna walk with the angels and sing round the throne

I'm going home on a cloud.

Weevily Wheat

American traditional

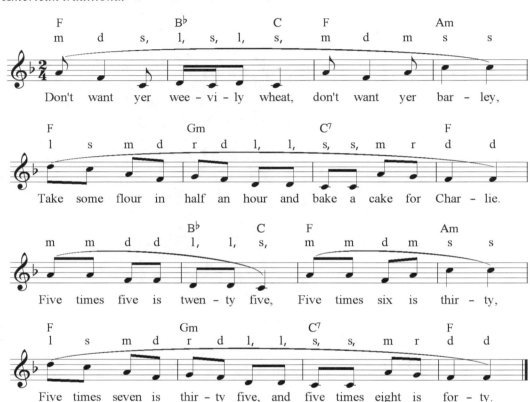

Don't want yer wee-vi-ly wheat, don't want yer bar-ley,

Take some flour in half an hour and bake a cake for Char-lie.

Five times five is twen-ty five, Five times six is thir-ty,

Five times seven is thir-ty five, and five times eight is for-ty.

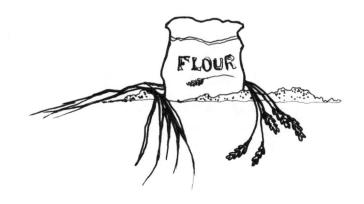

Teaching Tips

- Teach by rote. This cheerful song is pentatonic and, like much pentatonic material, it works well in canon one bar or one line apart, and in augmentation.

- Try adding these amusing vocal ostinatos for an exciting arrangement. Start off with the rhythms only, chanted, clapped or played on a percussion instrument.

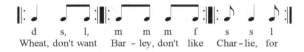

Wheat, don't want Bar-ley, don't like Char-lie, for

- The ideas for arrangement above should not be combined with the suggested chordal accompaniment, which uses different harmonies.

- With its full use of the pentatonic scale and steps of the *do* chord, this song is useful material for dictation or work with stick notation.

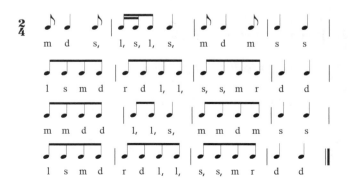

L' Inverno l'è Passato (*Winter has passed*)

Italian Swiss folk-song

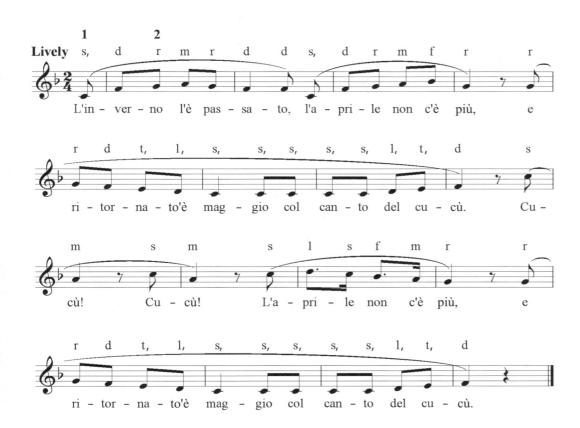

Teaching Tips

- The Italian is not difficult to master. Teach by rote, pronouncing each syllable as it is written.
    - 'c' before an i or e is pronounced 'ch'
    - 'c' before a, o or u is pronounced 'k'
    - 'gg' is pronounced like a j

- Point out the similarity to the English in the words *passato* (passed), *aprile* (April), *maggio* (May) and, of course, *cucù* (cuckoo).

- The song may be sung in canon, as indicated, or you may prefer to have a small group echoing the "Cucù" each time it is sung.

- For a longer performance, the melody can be played by a good recorder player in between two sung verses.

- The opening rhythm of the F - G quavers is sometimes dotted. This is shown in stick notation in the preliminary section of the book on page xi.

Translation

Winter has passed, April is gone.

May has returned with the singing of the cuckoo.

The Fiddler

Swabian folk-song. English text by Alfred Body

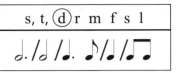

2   Such magic has his music that birds in the sky
    When they hear it, come in thousands and dance up on high

    So, come and join the dance etc.

3   Soon everybody's dancing, all charmed by the skill
    Of the wonderful fiddler just over the hill.

    So, come and join the dance, etc.

Teaching Tips

- This song has a lovely swing to it, and is good for getting the feel of $\frac{3}{4}$ metre, with some useful examples of ♩. (*ta-a-a*) and ♪. (*ta-e*).

- The underlying harmonies lend themselves to a simple bass line on the open strings of a cello, or guitar chords (one note or chord per bar):

‖: G : G : D : G :‖   ‖: G : C : G : D : G :‖

Hari Coo Coo

Indian lullaby

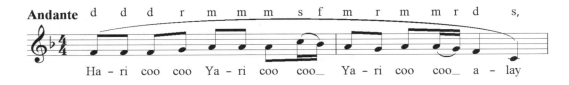

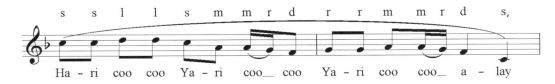

Teaching Tips

- The words are repetitive but contain a surprising memory test: is it *Hari* or *Yari* at the end of each line? See if the children can discover a pattern.

- This can be sung in canon a half-bar apart.

- Use movement with this song. Gentle rocking or swaying on the beat conveys the mood of a lullaby. Feel the phrase length by walking each four-bar phrase, changing direction as the next phrase starts.

Dona Dona Dona

Words and music by Sholom Secunda.
English translation by A. Kevess and T. Schwartz

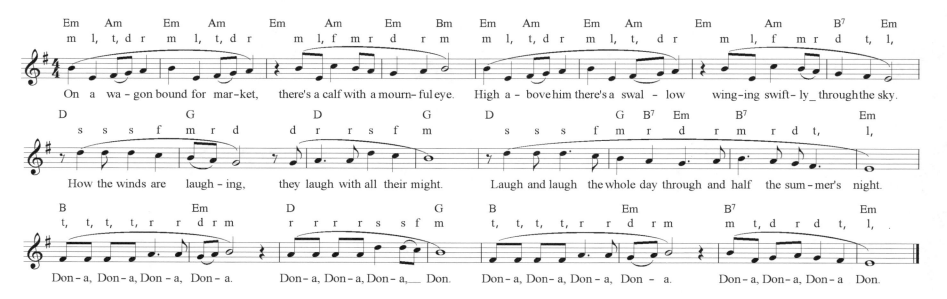

On a wa - gon bound for mar-ket, there's a calf with a mourn-ful eye. High a - bove him there's a swal - low wing-ing swift- ly through the sky.

How the winds are laugh - ing, they laugh with all their might. Laugh and laugh the whole day through and half the sum-mer's night.

Don - a, Don - a, Don - a, Don - a. Don - a, Don - a, Don - a, Don. Don - a, Don - a, Don - a, Don - a. Don - a, Don - a, Don - a Don.

Teaching Tips

- This song is a good example of the natural minor or Aeolian mode.

- There are three clear sections, each starting with an interesting rhythm which can be used as an ostinato accompaniment:

The children can experiment with where to use these ostinatos through the song, and try different percussion instruments to highlight the three sections.

- A very simple constant pattern to use together with the other ostinatos is:

2 "Stop complaining", said the farmer,
"Who told you a calf to be?
Why don't you have wings to fly with
Like the swallow so proud and free?"

How the winds etc.

3 Calves are easily bound and slaughtered
Never knowing the reason why,
But whoever treasures freedom
Like the swallow has learned to fly

How the winds etc.

The Poor Stranger

Southern Irish folk-song, with thanks to Bill Meek.
Reproduced with permission of Ossian Publications Ltd, Cork, Ireland

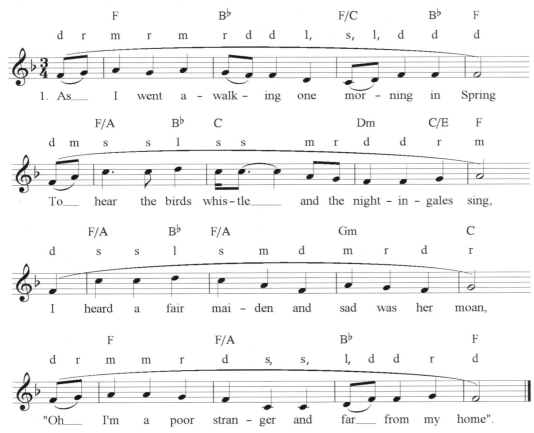

2   I'll build my love a cottage at the edge of this town
    Where the Lords, Dukes and Earls they will not knock it down.
    And if the boys ask her why she lives alone,
    She'll say she's a stranger and far from her home.

Teaching Tips

■ The chords given here are only, as always with folk-songs, a guide. Songs like this stand up very well on their own, and chordal accompaniments, unless very subtle, can detract from the beauty of the melody line. The song is very suitable performed as a solo.

■ The chord notation makes use of the shorthand F/A to indicate a chord of F major with A as the lowest note, ie. in first inversion. Listen to the chord in root position and compare with the sound of the first inversion.

■ Guitarists may find the chordal accompaniment easier to play in G major. The new chord sequence can be worked out as a transposition exercise. Every chord should be a full tone or major second higher (F to G, etc.).

■ As with most pentatonic material, melodic motifs taken from the song can be used to create an ostinato accompaniment, as an alternative to the chords. Here are a few to try.

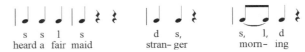

■ This is good material for work with stick notation.

Poor Wayfaring Stranger

Southern White Spiritual

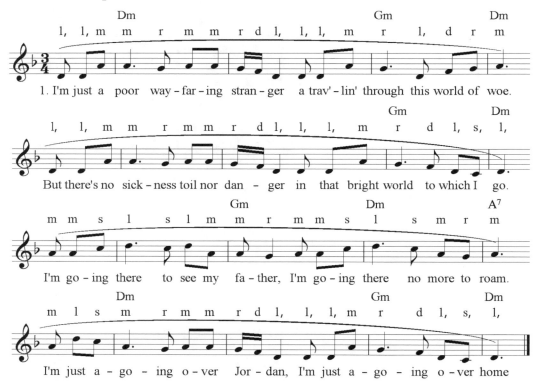

1. I'm just a poor way–far–ing stran–ger a trav'–lin' through this world of woe.

But there's no sick–ness toil nor dan – ger in that bright world to which I go.

I'm go – ing there   to see my   fa – ther, I'm go – ing there   no more to roam.

I'm just a – go – ing o – ver   Jor – dan, I'm just a – go – ing o – ver home

2 I know dark clouds will gather round me,
   I know my way is rough and steep,
   But beauteous fields lie just beyond me
   Where souls redeemed their vigil keep.
   I'm going there to meet my mother.
   She said she'd meet me when I come.
   I'm only going over Jordan,
   I'm only going over home.

3 I want to wear a crown of glory,
   When I get home to that bright land.
   I want to shout Salvation's story,
   In concert with that Bloodwashed band.
   I'm going there to meet my Saviour,
   To sing his praise for evermore.
   I'm only going over Jordan,
   I'm only going over home.

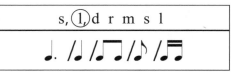

Teaching Tips

■ The words of this beautiful *la* pentatonic song express the main theme of the spiritual, the anguish over the toil and woes of this harsh world, and the longing for the next. It must be sung with deep feeling.

■ Use very simple harmonies to enhance the song. Add variety to individual verses in any of the following ways:

– use an open fifth for each chord instead of the full harmony

– sustain a D minor harmony throughout

– use a single note (D, G, etc) to accompany each bar instead of the full chord. This can be played on the open strings of a cello or guitar.

■ The rhythm throughout is very regular. This steady off-beat ostinato accompaniment would help children feel the ♪ ♫ upbeat and the full length of the dotted crotchet:

How Can I Keep From Singing?

This traditional song reflects the early struggles of the Quakers. It is reportedly from North Carolina, but has also been traced to Indiana, perhaps arriving there with the migrations during the early 1800s.

Old Quaker hymn. American traditional

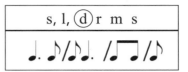

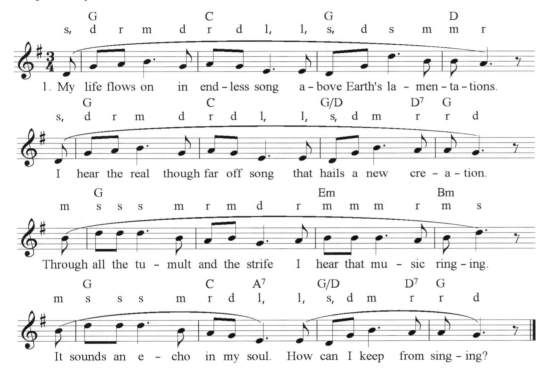

2 What though the tempest loudly roars,
   I hear the truth, it liveth;
   What though the darkness round me close,
   Songs in the night it giveth.
   No storm can shake my inmost calm
   While to that rock I'm clinging,
   Since love is lord of heaven and earth,
   How can I keep from singing?

3 When tyrants tremble as they hear
   The bells of freedom ringing;
   When friends rejoice, both far and near,
   How can I keep from singing?
   In prison cell and dungeon vile
   Our thoughts are to them winging;
   When friends by shame are undefiled,
   How can I keep from singing?

Teaching Tips

■ The constantly occurring ♪ | ♩♩ ♩. rhythm and the gentle rise and fall of the melody creates a lovely flowing feel in this beautiful pentatonic song.

■ This is a very useful example of the ♩. ♪ (*ta-e te*) rhythm, which can be felt more clearly over a steady ♩ beat or ♩ ♩ pattern.

■ The song's constant rhythmic motif can be used as an ostinato pattern for percussion accompaniment, at a beat's distance from the melody:

Either: ‖: ♩. ♪♩♩ :‖   or   ‖: ♪ ♪♩♩♩ :‖
         ta-e te te te   te te te ta

■ Make a longer arrangement with an instrumental verse. The melody is very suitable for descant recorder or flute.

I've Been Working on the Railroad

It is doubtful that this is a pure folk-song, but it is very popular with boys.

American traditional

* Bracketed (optional alternative) chords

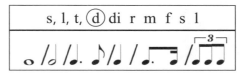

Teaching Tips

■ A jaunty work song with a typically strong pulse, inviting marching to the ♩ (*ta*) beat, or other rhythmic action on the minim pulse (eg, coal shovelling).

■ Especially good for the two main types of dotted rhythm ♩. ♪ (*ta-e te*) and ♩. ♫ (*temri*), which can be felt more clearly when the pulse is marked.

■ The chord pattern has been kept very simply to the three primary chords I, IV and V (G, C and D), which can be played on keyboard or guitar, or as single notes on the open strings of a cello. Alternative harmonies are given in brackets.

■ As a lesson in chord building, the children can work out what steps of the scale they need for each primary chord and find them on a set of chime bars in G major. This makes another nice way to accompany the song, and is a good small group activity.

■ The section beginning "Someone's in the kitchen with Dinah" combines well with the following section "Fee fi".

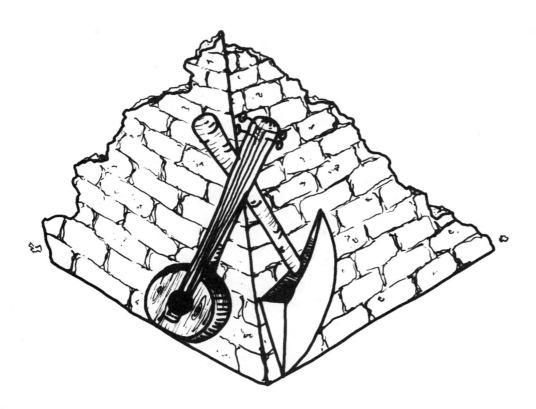

10 Folk-Songs of the British Isles

Kodály believed that folk-songs from our own culture should be the basis of our musical growth and experience. They are part of our musical heritage, and spring from our own language. In using them, learning to sing is as natural as learning to speak.

In our multi-ethnic society we are able to draw on the folk traditions of many cultures. In making our choice of songs for this book we have had a wealth of repertoire to choose from.

Britain has a strong tradition of folk music. At the beginning of the twentieth century Cecil Sharp, and composers like Vaughan Williams, George Butterworth and Edward Moeran, went about the country listening to singers and collecting songs, singing games and country dances. As a result of this, there are many old collections of folk songs available. However, in recent times, these have been discarded as "old fashioned" in favour of compositions written in a more modern idiom with words that are more relevant to today's children.

We feel it is important to choose songs which still have a direct appeal, either through the story they tell, the connection with events in history, or simply for their beauty of line.

Oh No, John

This traditional English verse and chorus song can be acted out, with girls and boys singing appropriate verses.

English folk-song

On yon-der hill there stands a— crea-ture, who she is I do not know.

I'll go and court her for her_beau–ty. She must an-swer Yes or No.

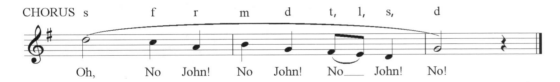

CHORUS

Oh, No John! No John! No— John! No!

Teaching Tips

■ The simple rhythmic elements in this song make it useful for teaching crotchets and minims through reading or dictation.

■ So many English folk-songs begin with the *s,–d* upbeat. This is an excellent example.

■ You can point out the rising and falling thirds and identify them as major or minor.

■ Work out an accompaniment with chords I, II, V and VI.

2 My father was a Spanish captain
   Went to sea a month ago,
   First he kissed me, then he left me,
   Bid me always answer No.
   Chorus

3 Oh Madam, in your face is beauty
   On your lips red roses grow,
   Will you take me for your husband?
   Madam, answer Yes or No.
   Chorus

4 Madam, since you are so cruel,
   And that you do scorn me so,
   If I may not be your husband,
   Madam, will you let me go?
   Chorus

5 Hark I hear the church bells ringing
   Will you come and be my wife?
   Or dear Madam, have you settled
   To live single all your life?
   Chorus

Migildi Magildi

This song was first noted from the singing of a Mr Richard Williams, who had learned it while he was a blacksmith's apprentice. Joe Wain, the blacksmith, frequently visited local farms in the evenings to amuse the farmers with his songs and poems. Dan Jackson, the "striker" at Joe Wain's smithy often danced to Joe's songs. Lyrics in *italic* are a pronunciation guide.

Welsh folk-song.
Reproduced with permission of the Welsh Folk Song Society.

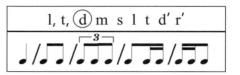

Ffeind a di-fyr yd-yw gwe-led, Mi-gil-di,*ma-gil-di, now now now.
(Find are dee-vir udd-ewe gooair led)*

Drws yr ef-ail yn a-gor-ed, Mi-gil-di, ma-gil-di, now now now.
(Droos err ev-aisle un are-gor-red)

A'r go' bach a'i wyn-eb pur-ddu, Mi-gil-di, ma-gil-di, now now now,_
(Are_ gor barch aye wee-nebpeer-thee)*

Yn yr ef-ail yn pry-sur chwy-thu, Mi-gil-di, ma-gil-di, now now now.
(Un err ev-aisle un pru-seer ch-worthy)

Teaching Tips

■ Use the *Migildi Magildi* refrain to show that your crotchet beat can be divided into either two or three quavers. Feel the strong pulse through movement, eg, stepping, while clapping the quavers evenly.

■ Find out more about the role of the village blacksmith in cross-curricular work.

* Pronunciation Guide

Mígildi, mágildi: Stress falls on *first* syllable

udd = as in udder
ch = guttural sound

Translation

It is pleasant to see the door of the smithy open
And the little smith with his coal black face
Busily blowing in the smithy.
It is pleasant during the long winter nights
To be the first to run to the smithy
When it's frosty and snowing outside,
And to sit by the warm hearth.

Children's Dance

There is a children's dance to this song, which falls in three sections. Section A works well on its own as a very simple dance. When this is secure, you can add sections B and C, which must be performed together for the R and L steps to work out correctly.

First teach these basic dance steps:

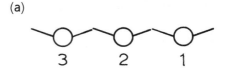

(a)

1. BS (R) = basic step leading with R foot. (BS (L) = basic step leading with L foot.)

    1st bar   ♪   Step forward on R

                  ♪   Close L to R transferring weight

                  ♪   Step forward on R

                  ♪   Hop, lifting L leg

    2nd bar   Repeat, leading with other foot

                            (In the dance, this step is also performed backwards.)

(b)

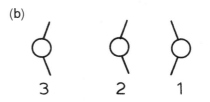

2. Stamp (R) = stamping rhythm leading with R foot. (Stamp (L) = stamping rhythm with L foot.)

                 ♩ ♩   Two stamps forward, R then L foot

                 ♫ ♩   Three stamps in quick time on the spot, R, L, R

(c)

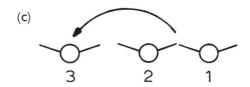

Dance Formation

The children form into lines of three standing side by side, inside hands joined, facing front (*see* **a**)

A	Bars 1–2	BS(R) (2 bars)
	Bars 3–4	Stamp (R)
	Bars 5–8	BS(L) (4 bars) backwards
	Bars 9–14	(Figure of 8)
		1 and 2 face each other, and 3 faces 2 (*see* **b**)
		1 and 2 begin, BS(L) (6 bars), passing first with the R shoulder
		3 joins in, passing first with L shoulder.
		Finish in line facing forward (*see* **a**)
	Bars 15–16	Stamp (L)
B	Bars 1–4	1 and 2 hold inside hands and "visit" 3, BS(R) (4 bars) (*see* **c**)
	Bars 5–8	3 joins in (*see* **d**) and all circle to R, BS(R) (4 bars), finishing in a straight line sideways on (*see* **e**)
	Bars 9–12	BS(R) (4 bars)
	Bars 13–14	BS(R) (2 bars) backwards, swinging round to face front again (*see* **a**)
	Bars 15–16	Stamp (R)
C	Bars 1–8	Repeat B with 2 and 3 "visiting" 1, BS(L) (4 bars), circling L, BS(L) (4 bars), to make straight line sideways on, facing opposite way (*see* **f**)
	Bars 9–12	BS(L) (2 bars)
		Stamp (L)
	Bars 13–16	BS(R) (4 bars) backwards, swinging round to finish facing front (*see* **a**)

(d)

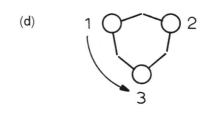

(e)   (f)

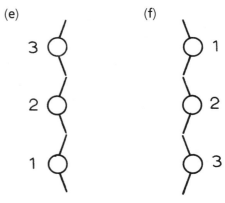

Blow Away the Morning Dew

With its jaunty tune and dotted rhythm in the chorus, this song is deceptively cheerful until the bittersweet last verse.

Somerset folk-song

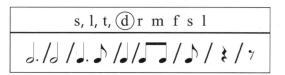

Teaching Tips

■ Useful for teaching the notes below d.

■ Note the upbeat *s,–s,–d* with the accent on the second *s*, rather than the more common *s,–d*.

■ Point out the interval of the minor seventh (*s,–f* in bars 7–8).

■ Note the major triad (*s–m–d*) in bar 13, followed by the relative minor (*m–d–l,*) in bar 14.

■ This song was used by Vaughan Williams in his *Folk Song Suite* for Military Band.

2 She gathered to her lovely flow'rs
And spent her time in sport,
As if in pretty Cupid's bow'rs
She daily did resort
Chorus

3 The yellow cowslip by the brine
The daffodil as well
The timid primrose, pale and trim
The pretty snowdrop bell
Chorus

4 She's gone with all those flowers sweet
Of white and red and blue,
And unto me about my feet
Is only left the rue
Chorus

The Sweet Nightingale

The verses of this courting song can be divided between boys and girls, according to the words.

English folk-song

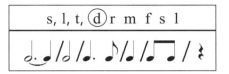

2 Pretty Betty, don't fail,
For I'll carry your pail
Safe home to your cot as we go.
You shall hear..

3 Pray let me alone,
I have hands of my own,
Along with your Sir, I'll not go.
For to hear..

4 Pray sit yourself down
With me on the ground
On this bank where the primroses grow.
You shall hear..

5 The couple agreed and were married with speed
And soon to the church they did go.
No more is she afraid for to walk in the shade,
Or to sit in those valleys below....

Teaching Tips

■ Pay attention to the phrasing, using one breath to each phrase. You will notice that not one phrase is actually repeated.

■ The rhythmic elements are very straightforward. Notice the sequential treatment of the dotted crotchets in the lovely penultimate phrase.

■ Another example of the *s,–d* upbeat but with the *s,* repeated to make a recurring rhythmic motif:

Ask the class to identify it each time they hear it.

■ A good song for teaching the meaning of the expression marks.

■ Can be harmonised using just chords I, IV and V if preferred.

The Keel Row

This popular Northumbrian song is a great favourite with singers of all ages. A "keel" is a coal barge.

Northumbrian folk-song.
With thanks to Boosey & Hawkes

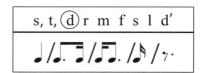

Teaching Tips

■ Teach the dotted rhythms:

■ The ostinato should be played on a bass instrument and is a good introduction to the tonic, dominant and subdominant chords. (I, V, IV). Children learning the piano, keyboard or guitar will enjoy working these out on their instruments.

■ Others may like to improvise an ostinato on untuned percussion instruments, using the newly learned dotted rhythms to emphasise the movement of the boat.

2　Oh who's like my Johnny, sae leish, sae blithe, sae bonny,
　　He's foremost of the mony keel lads o'coaly Tyne.
　　He'll set and row so tightly, or in the dance so sprightly,
　　He'll cut and shuffle sightly, 'tis true, were he not mine.

3　He wears a blue bonnet, blue bonnet, blue bonnet,
　　He wears a blue bonnet, a dimple in his chin.
　　And weel may the keel row, the keel row, the keel row,
　　O weel may the keel row that my laddie's in.

The Jug of Punch

This jolly Irish tune with its nonsense syllables in the chorus is quickly learned.

Irish traditional, with thanks to Bucks Music Ltd, London

Teaching Tips

- Use some of the rhythmic patterns as a rhythmic dictation.

- Point out the upbeat in each phrase, and the *syncopa* in bar 1.

- Try the ostinato on an instrument or have a small group sing it in solfa.

2 What more diversion can a man desire
Than to court a girl by a neat turf fire,
With a Kerry pippin to crack an'crunch
Aye, an'on the table a jug of punch.

3 The learned doctors with all their art,
Cannot cure the impression that's on the heart,
Even the gambler forgets his hunch
When he's safe outside of a jug of punch.

4 And when I'm dead and in my grave,
No costly tombstone will I crave,
Just lay me down in my native peat
With a jug of punch at my head and feet.

93

Kelvin Grove

The verses of this lively Scottish song tell a sad story of the soldier who says goodbye to his sweetheart, fearing he might never return from the battlefield.

Scottish tradtitional song, words by Lyle. With thanks to Boosey & Hawkes

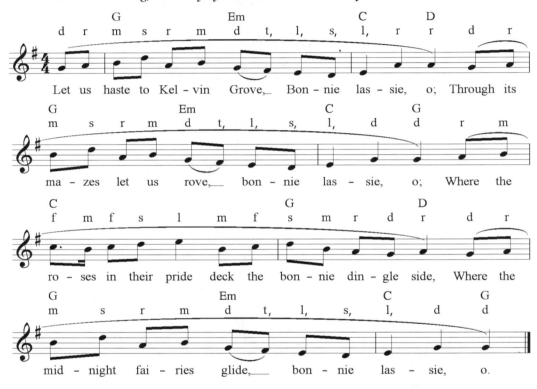

Teaching Tips

■ This has a very simple rhythmic structure (AABA). Use it for dictation (spot the dotted rhythm!)

■ The phrases can be easily recognised and analysed.

■ Note the plagal cadence (IV–I) at the end of the second and fourth phrases, which is useful preparation for higher grade aural tests.

2   Though I dare not call thee mine, bonnie lassie, O
      As the smile of fortune's thine, bonnie lassie, O
      Yet with fortune on my side, I could stay thy father's pride,
      And win thee for my bride, bonnie lassie, O.

3   But the frowns of fortune lour, bonnie lassie, O,
      On thy lover at this hour, bonnie lassie, O,
      Ere yon golden orb of day wake the warblers on the spray,
      From this land I must away, bonnie lassie, O.

4   Then farewell to Kelvin Grove, bonnie lassie, O,
      And adieu to all I love, bonnie lassie, O,
      To the river winding clear, to the fragrant scented brier,
      E'en to thee of all most dear, bonnie lassie, O.

5   When upon a foreign shore, bonnie lassie, O,
      Should I fall midst battle's roar, bonnie lassie, O,
      Then, Helen, shouldst thou hear of thy lover on his bier
      To his memory shed a tear, bonnie lassie, O.

Searching for Lambs

There are many English folk-songs with this title but different words. Cecil Sharp, in whose collection of *100 English Folksongs* it is found, writes: "The tune is modal, but lacking the sixth of the scale, it may be either Aeolian or Dorian..... The words are almost exactly as they were sung to me. Taking words and tune together, I consider this to be a very perfect example of a folk song".

English folk-song

2 What makes you rise so soon, my dear
   Your journey to pursue?
   Your pretty little feet they tread so sweet,
   Strike off the morning dew.

3 I'm going to feed my father's flock,
   His young and tender lambs,
   That over hills and over dales
   Lie waiting for their dams.

4 O stay! O stay! you handsome maid
   And rest a moment here,
   For there is none but you alone
   That I do love so dear.

5 For I am thine, and thou are mine
   No man shall uncomfort thee,
   We'll join our hands in wedded bands
   And a married we will be.

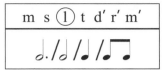

Teaching Tips

■ Sing this quite freely with a very legato singing line. A gentle sustained chord on *l,–m* makes a simple and effective accompaniment to each phrase.

■ You might introduce the $\frac{5}{4}$ timing through some kind of movement, allowing the children to discover for themselves that bar 4 is different.

■ Compare the *m,–l,* upbeat to the major *s,–d* in "Oh No, John".

The Black Velvet Band

This rollicking song is a warning to all brave, young Irish lads to beware of pretty young damsels! You could act it out.

Irish traditional. With thanks to Ossian Publcations Ltd, Cork, Ireland

1. As I went walk-ing down Broad-way,___ not in-tend-ing to stay ve-ry long,___ I met with a fro-lick-some dam-sel as she came a-trip-ping a-long.___ A watch she took out of her pock-et___ and slipped it right in-to my hand.___ On the ve-ry first day that I met___ her; bad luck to the black vel-vet band.___ Her

CHORUS

eyes they shone___ like dia-monds___ I thought her the queen of the land.___ And her hair hung o-ver her shoul – der tied up with a black vel-vet band.___

* Bracketed chords optional

96

2   'Twas in the town of Tralee an apprentice to trade I was bound
    With a-plenty of bright amusement to see the days go round
    Till misfortune and trouble came over me, which caused me to stray from my land
    Far away from my friends and relations, to follow the Black Velvet Band.

3   Before the judge and the jury the both of us had to appear,
    And a gentleman swore to the jewellery – the case against us was clear,
    For seven years transportation right unto Van Dieman's Land
    Far away from my friends and relations, to follow her Black Velvet Band.

4   Oh all you brave young Irish lads, a warning take by me,
    Beware of the pretty young damsels that are knocking around in Tralee
    They'll treat you to whiskey and porter, until you're unable to stand
    And before you have time for to leave them, you are unto Van Dieman's Land.

s, l, t, (d) r m f s

Teaching Tips

- This can be used as a good example of rhythms in compound time:

- The tune is straightforward, and can be accompanied by simple guitar chords

The Diamond

This song, about the Peterhead ship, *The Diamond*, dates from the 1820s when the Greenland Sea was so heavily fished that whales became scarce. In 1830, there occurred one of the greatest disasters of British whaling, when twenty ships, including *The Diamond*, *The Eliza Swan* and *The Resolution*, were lost, trapped in the ice of Melville Bay.

Scottish folk-song, arranged by Douglas Coombes from Sing Around the World,
with permission of Lindsay Music (© Lindsay Music 1996)

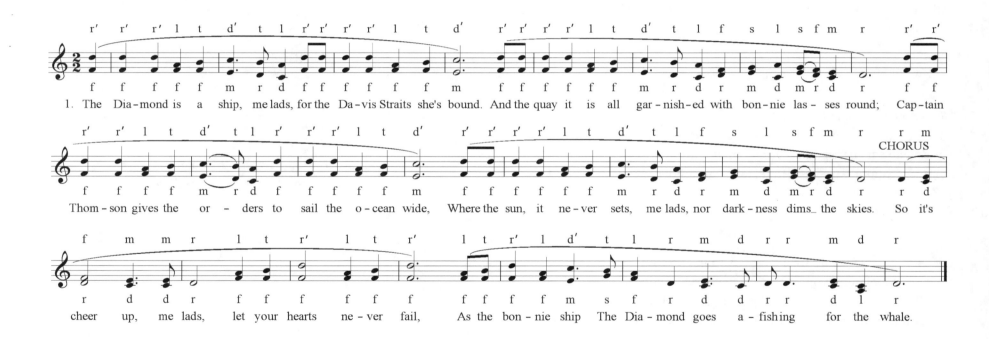

1. The Dia-mond is a ship, me lads, for the Da-vis Straits she's bound. And the quay it is all gar-nish-ed with bon-nie las-ses round; Cap-tain

Thom-son gives the or-ders to sail the o-cean wide, Where the sun, it ne-ver sets, me lads, nor dark-ness dims the skies. So it's

CHORUS

cheer up, me lads, let your hearts ne-ver fail, As the bon-nie ship The Dia-mond goes a-fishing for the whale.

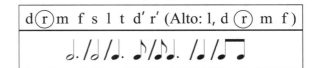

Teaching Tips

■ This song is a good example of the Dorian mode. See Page 48 for an explanation of the Dorian scale.

■ Play a simple accompaniment on a low instrument using only the notes D and A, to reinforce the tonality.

■ The alto part uses a limited number of notes and would provide a challenge to more able pupils, both in reading and in singing the part.

■ Use a bass drum or tambour to play an ostinato in the verses. Change to different instruments for the Chorus, using any of these rhythms:

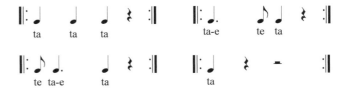

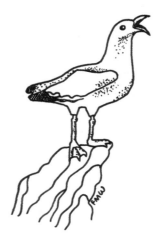

2 Along the quay at Peterhead
    The lasses stand around
    With their shawls all pulled about them
    And the salt tears running down;
    Don't you weep, my bonnie lasses,
    Though you be left behind,
    For the rose will grow on Greenland's ice
    Before we change our mind.   *Chorus*

3 Here's a health to the Resolution,
    Likewise the Eliza Swan,
    Here's a health to the Battler of Montrose
    And the Diamond, ship of fame.
    We wear the trousers of the white
    And the jackets of the blue,
    When we return to Peterhead
    We'll have sweethearts enough.   *Chorus*

4 It'll be bright both day and night
    When the Greenland lads come home
    With a ship that's full of oil, me lads,
    And money to our name;
    We'll make the cradles for to rock
    And the blankets for to tear
    And every lass in Peterhead
    Sing "hush-a-bye, my dear."   *Chorus*

Morag's Cradle Song

This gentle, rocking lullaby in **6/8** time uses the Mixolydian scale, ending on *s*. This is typical of many Scottish songs.

Traditional Gaelic lullaby

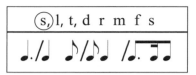

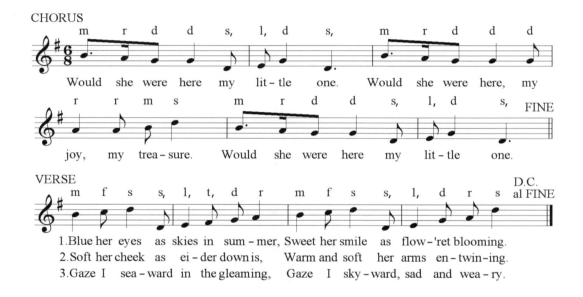

CHORUS

Would she were here my lit-tle one. Would she were here, my

joy, my trea-sure. Would she were here my lit-tle one.

VERSE

1. Blue her eyes as skies in sum-mer, Sweet her smile as flow-'ret blooming.
2. Soft her cheek as ei-der down is, Warm and soft her arms en-twin-ing.
3. Gaze I sea-ward in the gleaming, Gaze I sky-ward, sad and wea-ry.

Teaching Tips

- Point out the dotted rhythm

and the more unusual

- Notice how the chorus has descending motifs, whereas in the verses they are ascending. Be careful not to accent the last notes of the ascending phrases, before breathing for the next phrase.

- Try the following ostinato:

Lul - la - by,   Lul - la - by,

Glossary

The meanings of the words below apply to their usage in this book; this is not necessarily definitive.

Accelerando	Getting faster.
Augmentation	At half speed.
Cadence	Close of a phrase or piece of music formed by two chords. eg, perfect cadence is chords V–I, plagal cadence is chords IV–I.
Calypso	Traditional West Indian folk dance, now usually sung.
Canon	A form of composition for two or more voices (or instruments). A harmonised arrangement is created from a single line of music when successive voices start in imitation at a specified point of entry.
Catch	A round with witty and amusing words.
Chord	Two or (usually) more notes played or sung together. Chords can be built on every step (or *degree*) of a scale, each identified by number (I, II, III, etc.) or by the solfa name of the degree which is the root of the chord.. eg, *do* chord is the notes *d–m–s* sounded together, making the key chord of a major key, otherwise known as chord I.
Chromatic notes	Alterations, by sharps or flats, to the diatonic notes of a scale. eg, *fa* can be sharpened to *fi*, one semitone higher.
Compound time	"Skipping" rhythm, felt when the pulse is divided into three parts instead of two. Compound 2 time ($\frac{6}{8}$) occurs frequently in British children's songs, traditional rhymes and dances eg, *Here we go round the Mulberry Bush*, *Humpty Dumpty*.
Crescendo	Getting louder.
Descant	A pleasing treble melody, higher than and complementary to the main melody.
Diatonic music	Music using only the notes of the solfa scale, with no additional sharps or flats.
Dolce	Sweetly.
Dominant	The fifth step of the scale.
Dominant seventh chord (V7)	Chord built on the dominant or *so* degree, with the addition of the seventh note above *so* (*s–t–r–f*).
Drone	One or two notes repeated continuously as an accompaniment, usually the first and fifth notes of the scale, ie. *d* and *s* in a major key or *l* and *m* in a minor key.
Dynamics	Variations of tone and expression in music. Changes in volume.
Ensemble	Togetherness in musical performance.
Forte (*f*)	Loud. Fortissimo (*ff*), very loud.
Hexachord	A range of six adjacent notes of a scale. eg, *do* hexachord – the range *d r m f s l*.
Hocketing	Taking turns to clap on the beat.
Intonation	(i) Playing or singing with careful and accurate tuning. (ii) Good instrumental or vocal tone.
Interval	Distance between two different pitches. eg, the interval between *do* and *mi* (the first to the third step of a major scale) is a major third.
Inversion	A chord rearranged. eg, The *do* chord (*d–m–s*) is built on *do*: in this arrangement, with *do* as the lowest note, it is in root position. It can be rearranged as *m–s–d'* (first inversion) or *s–d'–m'* (second inversion).

101

Legato	Playing or singing smoothly, with joined or connected notes.
Modes	The forerunners of modern scales. Each step of the solfa ladder is the starting point of a modal scale with its own characteristic mood. eg, The Dorian mode is built on *re*: *r m f s l t d' r'*
Metre	The grouping of pulse into strong and weak beats, defining the music as 2, 3, or 4 time.
Ostinato	A musical motif, either rhythmic or melodic, often used as an accompaniment.
Patsch	Flat-palmed percussive slap, usually on knees or thighs. The word is derived from Orff Schulwerk.
Pentatonic	Five sounds (= *d r m s l*). This gapped scale can easily be explored on the black notes of a keyboard instrument. A *do* pentatonic melody is a pentatonic melody ending on *do*. (Music with fewer pitches can be defined as bi-, tri-, or tetratonic).
Pentachord	A range of five adjacent notes of a scale. eg, *la* pentachord – the range *l t d' r' m'*.
Phrase	One "unit" or idea in a musical sentence.
Piano (*p*)	Softly. Pianissimo (*pp*), very soft.
Pulse	The fundamental and constant beat felt in music, by which metre and rhythm is measured.
Quodlibet	A combination of two or more songs which fit together pleasingly in simultaneous musical performance.
Relative major and minor	Interrelated keys sharing the same *do*. *Do* is the key-note of the major key and *la* the key-note of the relative minor.
Round	A canon for two or (usually) more voices, whose starting points are equally distributed through the piece. At the end, each voice starts again, ad infinitum.
Rhythm	The pattern of sounds in music. Rhythm is transcribed in notes and rests of different lengths.
Semitone	*see* Tones and semitones.
Staccato	Short, detached playing or singing. Notes are not joined.
Swing rhythm	The custom in jazz, gospel music and some modern styles, to perform equal quavers ♪♪ (*tete*) or the ♪. ♪ (*temri*) rhythm as ♩ ♪ ("*doo-bee*"). This gives a more relaxed, improvisatory feel to a piece.
Syncopation	Displacement of the normal accent in a bar, generally by performing a note slightly earlier than the beat.
Tempo	Speed, rate of pulse in music.
Tones and semitones	The intervals between the pitches in a scale: *d r m f s l t d'*. *m–f* and *t–d'* are semitone steps (ie. half tones). All the other steps are tones. It is the arrangement of tones and semitones that makes the characteristic sounds of major and minor scales (centred on *do* and *la*) and modes, (centred on other steps of the solfa scale).
Tonic chord	The key-chord of the music (chord I).
Transposing	Moving a piece of music into another key.
Transposing instrument	An instrument which reads music in one key and pitches the notes in another key. eg, a clarinet in B$^\flat$ reads music written in C and pitches it in B$^\flat$. An alto sax in E$^\flat$ reads music written in C and pitches it in E$^\flat$.
Triad	A three-note chord built on any step of the scale. eg, *d–m–s*.
Upbeat	The unaccented note(s) before the main beat of a piece, phrase or bar.

Useful Contacts

British Kodály Academy
13 Midmoor Road
London SW19 4JD
Tel: 020 8971 2062
Fax: 020 8946 6561
www.britishkodalyacademy.org
Email: enquiries@britishkodalyacademy.org

BKA Bookstore
Contact BKA as above. See full Booklist on BKA website

Colourstrings and The Szilvay Foundation
One, The Tatt
Yalding
Kent
ME18 6HT
UK
Tel / Fax: 01622 815578
www.colourstrings.co.uk

Dalcroze Society (Inc.)
100 Elborough Street
London
SW18 5DL
Tel / Fax: 020 8870 1986
www.dalcroze.org.uk

English Folk Song and Dance Society
Cecil Sharp House
2 Regents Park Road
London
Tel: 020 7485 2206
www.efdss.org

International Kodály Society
H-1364 Budapest
P.O. Box 67
Hungary
Tel: +36-1-3434503
Fax: +36-1-4130138
Email: office@iks.hu

Kodály Centre of London
David Vinden
52 Highland Road
Northwood Hills
Middx HA6 1JU
Tel/Fax: 01923 821526
Email: david.vinden@talktalk.net

MUSICWorld
Douglas Coombes, Director
Lindsay Music
23 Hitchin Street
Biggleswade
Beds SG18 8AX
Tel: 01767 316521
Fax: 01767 317221
www.lindsaymusic.co.uk

Orff Society (UK)
7 Rothesay Avenue
Richmond
Surrey
TW10 5EB
Tel: 020 8876 1944
www.orff.org.uk

Voices Foundation
38 Ebury Street
London
SW1W 0LU
Tel: 020 7730 6677
www.voice.org/uk

Booklist

The following list of books and resources will give you ideas and useful material for developing your own musicianship training and that of your pupils, as well as extending your work in the classroom/instrumental lessons. *Available from the BKA Bookstore (see .p 103).

Appleby, William & Fowler, Frederick. *Sing Together*. Oxford University Press, Oxford. ISBN 0-19-330156-3.

A & C Black. *Apuskidu* (1975), *Alleluya* (1980), *Banana Splits* (1995), *Flying a Round* (1982), *Harlequin* (1981), *The Jolly Herring* (1980), *Sonsense Nongs* (1992), *Ta-ra-ra-boom-di-ay* (1977).
These are a few of the titles published in this attractive series. Available at your local music shops and some bookshops.

Brewer, Mike (1997). *Kick Start Your Choir*. Faber.
For help with all aspects of singing for choir leaders and directors.

Brocklehurst, Brian. *Pentatonic Song Book*; *Second Pentatonic Song Book*. Schott.

Choksy, Lois. * *The Kodály Method*. Prentice Hall, New Jersey. ISBN 0-13-516873-2.

Earl, Gillian. * *With Music in Mind. Teachers' Guide + Pupils' Books 1 and 2.*
Piano introductory course using Kodály approach.

Erdei, Peter & Komlos, Katalin. * *150 American Folksongs*. Boosey & Hawkes.

Forrai, Katalin. * *Music in Pre-School*. ISBN 963-1-3-3385-X.

Gaffney, Fiona (with contributions by Tom Oakshott). * *Music is for Everyone KS1–3 (age 7–11).*
Developed for use at Aysgarth School, this scheme of work includes songs, games, composition and a listening programme. Fiona Gaffney, Crossbank Hill, Hurworth-on-Tees, Darlington, DL2 2JB.

Herboly-Kocsár, Ildikó. * *Teaching of Polphony, Harmony and Form in Elementary School.*

Hill, David, & Parfitt, Hilary & Ashe, Elizabeth (1995). * *Giving Voice*. Kevin Mayhew.
A handbook for choir trainers.

Lindsay Music (arr. Douglas Coombes). * *Chay Chay Cooley*, * *Round the Classics*, * *Sing Around the World,* and other titles.
Lindsay Music, 23 Hitchin Street, Biggleswade, Beds, SG18 8AX. (see page 103)

Locke, Eleanor. * *Sail Away: 155 American Folksongs*. Boosey & Hawkes.

Manins, Stuart. * *So-Me Books 1 – 8 + tape.*
For reading with young children.

Molnár, Antal. * *Classical Canons EMB*. Boosey & Hawkes.

Simmons, Alan. Collections of part songs that children will enjoy singing, suitable for all Key Stages and specialising in encouraging boys to sing. Also good arrangements for mixed voices. Alan Simmons Music, PO Box 7, Scissett, Huddersfield HD8 9YZ, Tel: 01484 860755; Fax: 01484 860756.

Simpson, Kenneth. * *77 Rounds and Canons; Let's Sing*. Novello.

Sing for Pleasure * *Junior Song Books*, including songs for younger children, as well as KS2 & 3. Also good arrangements for SAB (useful for teenagers and young choirs) and SATB. Sing for Pleasure, Nortonthorpe Mills, Wakefield Road, Scissett, Huddersfield, HD8 9LA; Tel: 0800 0184 164.

Stocks, Michael & Maddocks, Andrew (1992). * *Growing with Music*, Teachers' Books 1, 2A & 2B. Pupils' book's 1–4. Longman. Available through The Voices Foundation, The Poets' House, 21 Earls Court Sq., London SW5 9BY.

Squires, Meredith. Musicianship Training Materials (stave cards, rhythm cards, counters, pitch reading cards, magnetic dry wipe board and marker). Available from Meredith Squires, Tel: 01494 670401.

Szönyi, Erzsébet. *Musical Reading and Writing, Teachers' Books I, II, & III and Pupils' Books 1–8. Boosey & Hawkes.

Vajda, Cecilia. The Kodály Way to Music, Parts 1 (1974) & 2 (1992). Boosey & Hawkes.

Vinden, David. * *Songs for Singing and Musicianship Training*; * *Musicianship through Singing*; * *A Little Collection of First Canons*; * *Making the Most of Your Material*; * *Sing * *2 part Canons* (for the development of two-part hearing); * *The Modes*; * *Flash Cards for Reading and Rhythm Training*. Kodály Centre of London (see page 103).

Kodály, Zoltán. * *50 Nursery Songs*; * *Pentatonic Music*, vols. I–IV; * *333 Exercises*; * *Bicinia Hungarica I &II*; * *77*, * *66*, * *55*, * *44*, * *33*, * *15 Exercises*; * *Tricinia*; * *Let Us Sing Correctly*; * *Epigrams*. Boosey & Hawkes.

Solfa Index

Songs are ordered according to the number of different pitches they contain. Songs with consecutive pitches in the solfa summary are listed before songs with non-consecutive pitches.

Minor

Songs with Chromatic Notes

Ta

Si

Fi

Di

Alphabetical Index of Songs with Musical Analysis

Title	Page	Origin/ Composer	Tone set	Tonality	Time signature	Rhythm set	Other features
'A' Melodic Minor Song	49	Fiona Gaffney	(l,) t, d r m f fi s si l	Melodic minor	4/4 2/2	(rhythm notation)	■ variations in tempo and dynamics ■ canon
Alabama Gal	3	American folk-song	(d) r m f s l	*do* hexachord	2/2	(rhythm notation)	■ A Av ■ movement ■ ostinato ■ syncopa
All Things Shall Perish	62	German folk-song	s, l, t, (d) r m f s l	Major	3/4	(rhythm notation)	■ quodlibet or two part canon ■ sequence ■ I II V7 I harmony
Alleluia	18	Michael Praetorius	d r m f s l t (d')	Major	4/4	(rhythm notation)	■ three-part canon ■ sequence ■ syncopa ■ stick notation
As I Was Walking	45	Traditional	r m f fi s l t (d')	Major + *fi*	2/4 6/8	(rhythm notation)	■ A B Av Bv ■ dance ■ ♪ upbeat
Ba-nu-wa	71	Liberian	d, f, s, (d) r m f s l t d' r' m' s'	Major	4/4	(rhythm notation)	■ multi-part ostinato ■ I IV V I harmony ■ optional improvisation ■ KS3
Bim Bam	36	Yiddish	(l,) t, d r m	*la* pentachord	2/2	(rhythm notation)	■ ostinato ■ accelerando ■ dance ■ ABBv

Title	Page	Composer/Source	Solfa	Mode	Time	Rhythm	Features
Bird of Heaven	54	Sydney Carter	m f s (l) t d' r' m' Alto: + d r si	Aeolian	2/4	♩ / ♩ / ♫ / ♩. ♫ / ♫. / ♫♫	• verse and chorus • optional second part • transposition
The Black Velvet Band	96	Irish folk-song	s, l, t, (d) r m f s	Major	6/8	♩. ♪ / ♩ ♪ / ♪ ♩ / ♫♫ / ♫ / ♪ / ↄ	• anacrusis • verses and refrain • chordal or bass line accompaniment
Blow Away the Morning Dew	90	Somerset folk-song	s, l, t, (d) r m f s l	Major	4/4	♩. / ♩ / ♩. ♪ / ♩ / ♫ ♪ / ♪ ↄ / ↄ	• anacrusis • verses and refrain • listening material • chordal accompaniment
Bravo, Bravo	62	Traditional	s, l, t, (d) r m f	Major	3/4	♩. / ♩ / ♩. ♪ / ♩	• two-part round • quodlibet • movement sequence • accompaniment
Chairs to Mend	66	William Hayes	d, f, t, (d) r m f s	Major	4/4	♩ / ♩. ♪ / ♩ ♪♪. / ♩ / ♫ / ♫.	• three-part catch • cross-curricular work using street cries • listening material
Che Che Kule	21	Ghanaian children's song	s, (l,) d	Tritonic	4/4	♩ / ♪♩ ♪ / ♫ / ♪ / ↄ	• echo song • action • composition exercise
Chicka Hanka	56	American folk-song	(l,) d r m	la tetratonic	2/4	♩ / ♪♩ ♪ / ♫ / ♫. / –	• A B C A • ostinato • quodlibet • syncopa
Chocolate Cake	11	Attributed to Ruth Edwards	d m s (d')	do chord	4/4	♩. ♪ / ♩ / ♫ / ↄ	• four-part round • tonic chord • stick notation
Christmas Round	13	Anonymous	s, (d) r m f s	do pentachord + s,	4/4	♩ / ♩. ♪ / ♩ / ♫	• four-part round • ostinatos • stick notation

Title	Page	Type	Solfa	Mode	Time	Rhythm	Features
Deryn y Bwn o'r Banna	9	Welsh folk-song	s, l, (d) r m f s	*do* hexachord + s, l,	6/8	(rhythm notation)	■ Welsh text ■ ostinatos
The Diamond	98	Scottish folk-song	d (r) m f s l t d' r' Alto: + l,	Dorian	2/2	(rhythm notation)	■ two-part harmonisation ■ rhythmic ostinatos ■ verse and chorus ■ upbeat
Ding Dong	42	American singing game	(d) m	Bitonic	2/4	(rhythm notation)	■ action game ■ accelerando ■ repeating motif
Dipidu	41	Ugandan traditional	(d) r m f s	*do* pentachord	3/4 2/4	(rhythm notation)	■ action ■ ostinato ■ AABB ■ stick notation
Dona Dona Dona	80	Sholom Secunda	(l,) t d r m f s	Aeolian	4/4	(rhythm notation)	■ verse and chorus ■ ostinatos
Down the River	28	Traditional	s, l, t, (d) r m f	Major	6/8	(rhythm notation)	■ two-part ■ stick notation
Duck Dance	43	American Indian	l, d r (m) s	*mi* pentatonic	4/4	(rhythm notation)	■ canon ■ augmentation ■ ostinato ■ movement
Everywhere We Go	22	Traditional chant	(s,) l, d m	Tetratonic	6/8	(rhythm notation)	■ echo song ■ variation in tempo and dynamic
Farewell	47	Hungarian folk-song	(l,) t, d r m	*la* pentachord	2/4	(rhythm notation)	■ A A B B ■ listening material

Title	Page	Source	Sol-fa	Mode	Time	Rhythm	Features
The Fiddler	78	Swabian folk-song	s, t, (d) r m f s l	Major	3/4	(rhythm notation)	■ chords I, IV and V ■ A Av B Bv ■ verse and refrain ■ sequence ■ ♩ upbeat
Fire Down Below	33	Traditional	m s (l) t d' r' m' (Lower part: + f, si)	Aeolian (no f)	2/4	(rhythm notation)	■ two-part
For All Thy Good Gifts	12	C. Benoit	d r m f s t (d')	Major (no l)	2/2	(rhythm notation)	■ three-part round ■ stick notation ■ ♩ upbeat
For Health and Strength	12	Brownie Prayer	s, t, (d) r m f s	Major (no l)	4/4	(rhythm notation)	■ four-part round ■ ♩ upbeat ■ sequence ■ stick notation
Grandma Grunts	4	American traditional	(d) r m s	do tetratonic	2/4	(rhythm notation)	■ d m s chord ■ ostinato ■ canon ■ stick notation ■ role play
Ha Ha Ha	67	Luigi Cherubini	m, s, l, t, (d) r m f s l	Major	4/4	(rhythm notation)	■ three-part canon ■ do chord ■ chords I and V ■ vocal agility (KS3)
Hari Coo Coo	79	Indian lullaby	s, (d) r m f s l	do hexachord + s,	2/4	(rhythm notation)	■ A A B B A A ■ canon ■ D.C. al Fine ■ movement
Hashivenu	70	Meir Ben Uri	l, t, d r m f (l) t d'	Aeolian (no s)	3/4	(rhythm notation)	■ three-part round ■ dynamic variation ■ legato singing
Heidi	50	Danish Girl Guide song	m, si, (l,) t, d r m f	Harmonic minor	2/4	(rhythm notation)	■ two-part round ■ optional dance movements

Title	Page	Source	Solfa	Mode/Scale	Time	Rhythm	Features
Hen Wraig Fach	8	Welsh folk-song	d r m f s l t (d') r' m'	Major	2/4		■ major scale ■ Welsh text ■ ostinatos ■ stick notation
Hey Dum Bar de Ay	31	Rainforest song	s, l, ta, (d) m f s	Mixolydian	2/2		■ large group activity ■ finger percussion rain sound ■ two part ostinato ■ dynamic contrasts
Hi Lo Chickalo	38	UK playground game	s, l, (d)	Tritonic	2/4		■ partner clapping game
Ho! Every Sleeper Waken	16	Traditional	s, (d) r m f s d'	*do* pentachord + *s, d'*	2/4		■ three-part round ■ *do* chord ■ chords I and V7 ■ ♪ upbeat
How Can I Keep From Singing?	83	Traditional American Quaker hymn	s, l, (d) r m s	*do* pentatonic	3/4		■ A Av B Av ■ ostinatos ■ ♪ upbeat
Hurry Hurry	64	Traditional calypso	m f s l t (d')	Major (no *r*)	4/4		■ quodlibet ■ rhythmic ostinato
In Praise of Solfa	67	Luigi Cherubini	s, t, (d) r m f s l t d'	Major	4/4		■ three-part canon ■ chords I and V ■ *do* chord ■ singing agility (KS3)
L'Inverno l'è Passato	77	Italian Swiss folk-song	s, l, t, (d) r m f s l	Major	2/4		■ I and V7 harmony ■ Italian text ■ A B C B ■ canon or echo ■ ♪ upbeat
I've Been Working on the Railroad	84	American traditional	s, l, t, (d) di r m f s l	Major + *di*	4/4		■ march ■ chords I, IV and V

Title	Page	Origin	Solfa	Mode	Time	Rhythm	Features
Janie Mama	68	Traditional calypso	s, l, t, (d) r m f s	Major	4/4	*(rhythm notation)*	• four-part round • I II V7 I chord progression • KS3
The Jug of Punch	93	Irish traditional	t, (d) r m f s l	Major	3/4	*(rhythm notation)*	• verse and refrain • ♪ upbeat • ostinato • chordal accompaniment
Kapa	40	Ugandan children's game	(d) r m s l	do pentatonic	4/4	*(rhythm notation)*	• action/game • ♪ upbeat
The Keel Row	92	Northumbrian traditional	s, t, (d) r m f s l d'	Major	2/4	*(rhythm notation)*	• A Av B Bv • verse and refrain • ostinato bassline
Keep Music Alive	11	Douglas Coombes	t, (d) r m f s l t d'	Major	4/4	*(rhythm notation)*	• four-part round • syncopation
Kelvin Grove	94	Scottish	s, l, t, (d) r m f s l	Major	4/4	*(rhythm notation)*	• A A B A • verse and refrain • plagal cadence
Li'l Liza Jane	60	American folk-song	(d) r m s l d'	do pentatonic	2/4	*(rhythm notation)*	• quodlibet • multiple ostinatos • augmentation • A Av B Bv
London Bridge is Falling Down	58	English traditional	(d) r m f s l	do hexachord	4/4	*(rhythm notation)*	• quodlibet • I and V7 harmony
Love Grows Under	44	Girl Guide singing game	(d) r m f s l t d'	Major	2/2	*(rhythm notation)*	• A B C C • action ostinato • accelerando

Love Somebody	2	American traditional	(d) r m f s	*do* pentachord	**2/4**	♩ / ♫	▪ A AvA B ▪ game ▪ *d s,* bassline
Ma, Ma, Will You Buy Me a Banana?	24	Canadian singing game	t, (d) r m f s d'	Major (no *l*)	**2/4**	♩ / ♫ / ♫ ♫	▪ A Av ▪ question/answer ▪ actions/role play ▪ humour
Migildi Magildi	88	Welsh folk-song	l, t, (d) m s l t d'r'	Major (no *f*)	**2/4**	♩ / ♫ /⌐3⌐ ♫♫ / ♫ ♫ / ♫ ♫	▪ A A B C ▪ Welsh text ▪ dance ▪ cross-curricular work
Missa Ram Goat	23	Jamaican folk-song	s, l, (d) r m s l	*do* pentatonic	**4/4**	♩ / ♩ / ♩♪ ♪/ ♫	▪ echo song ▪ ♫ upbeat ▪ ostinatos ▪ stick notation
Mr Scarfe's Action Round	37	Douglas Scarfe	(s,) l, t, d r m	*so* hexachord	**4/4**	♩. / ♩ / ♫	▪ action ostinato ▪ ♩ upbeat ▪ three-part round
Morag's Cradle Song	100	Traditional Gaelic	(s,) l, t, d r m f s	Mixolydian	**6/8**	♩. / ♩ ♪/ ♪ / ♪/ ♪ /♩. ♫	▪ verse and refrain ▪ ostinato
Mosquito Song	47	Hungarian dance tune	(l,) t, d r m	*la* pentachord	**4/4**	♩ / ♫	▪ four-part canon ▪ A A B Bv ▪ stick notation
Mountain Hike	27	Swiss Girl Guide song	s, l, t, (d) r m f s l	Major	**2/4**	♩ / ♫ / ♫ ♫	▪ two-part ▪ I and V harmony ▪ crescendo and diminuendo
The Mountains I Love	73	Swiss alpine song	s, l, t, (d) r m f s l Alto: + m, f,	Major	**3/4**	♩ / ♩. ♪/ ♩ / ♫	▪ two-part ▪ verse and refrain ▪ ostinato bassline ▪ chordal accompaniment

113

Title	Page	Origin/type	Solfa	Scale/mode	Time	Rhythm	Notes
No Need to Hurry	64	Traditional calypso	m f s l t (d') r'	Major	4/4	*(rhythm notation)*	■ quodlibet ■ rhythmic ostinatos ■ humour
Oh No, John	87	English traditional	s, l, t, (d) r m f s	Major	4/4	*(rhythm notation)*	■ verse and refrain ■ ♩ upbeat
Oi Dana	7	Polish dance song	s, (d) r m f s l	*do* hexachord + s,	3/4	*(rhythm notation)*	■ A B A C ■ stick notation ■ composition activity
Oncorrianda	39	UK playground game	(r) m f s l	*re* pentachord	2/4	*(rhythm notation)*	■ song & rhythmic chant ■ action ■ elimination game ■ internal ♫ upbeat
One' These Fine Mornings	75	Spiritual	(d) r m s l ta d'	*do* pentatonic + *ta*	2/4	*(rhythm notation)*	■ A B A C ■ verse and refrain ■ canon ■ ostinato
My Owlet	57	Kiowa Indian lullaby	(d) m s l	*do* tetratonic	2/4	*(rhythm notation)*	■ quodlibet ■ A A B B ■ two-part round ■ ostinatos
The Poor Stranger	81	Southern Irish folk-song	s, l, (d) r m s l	*do* pentatonic	3/4	*(rhythm notation)*	■ transposition ■ A B B A ■ ostinatos ■ stick notation ■ ♫ upbeat
Poor Wayfaring Stranger	82	Southern White spiritual	s, (l) d r m s l	*la* pentatonic	3/4	*(rhythm notation)*	■ A Av B Av ■ ♪ ♫ upbeat
Praise Him	17	Traditional gospel	m, s, l, (d) r m f	*do* pentatonic + *f*	4/4	*(rhythm notation)*	■ A B A C ■ four-part canon ■ swing rhythm ■ listening material

Title	Page	Source	Solfa	Mode/Scale	Metre	Rhythm	Features
Rainbow Girl	53	Chinese folk-song	s, (l,) d r m s l d'	*la* pentatonic	4/4	♩ /♪♪ ♪/♫ ♩/♩ ≀	■ A Av B C ■ syncopa ■ ostinato ■ optional canon
Rhythm Canon	35	Avon Gillespie	Unpitched		4/4	♩ /♫ ♩/ ≀	■ action ■ canon ■ optional tune
Rhythm Machine	35	Collected by Douglas Scarfe	Unpitched		4/4	♩ /♪ ♫ ♫/♫ ♫ /♫♫ ♫♫ /≀	■ voice percussion ■ action ■ group mime
Rise Up O Flame	48	Michael Praetorius	(l,) t, d r m l	*la* pentachord + *l*	3/4	♩. /♩. ♪/♩ ♩/♫	■ four-part canon
Rockin' By the Baby	57	American traditional	(d) r m s l	*do* pentatonic	2/4	♪. /♩ /♩/♫ /♩. ♫ /♩ /♫ ♫	■ quodlibet ■ verse and refrain ■ ostinatos
Rumanian Canon	48	Anonymous	(r) m f s l t	Dorian (no *d*)	4/4	♩ /♩ /♩/♫	■ three-part canon ■ repertoire in Dorian mode
Salut, Ça Va?	5	Nandita Hollins	(d) r m s	*do* tetratonic	2/4	♩. /♩ /♩/♫ /♪	■ stick notation ■ French text ■ ♪ upbeat
Seagull Sit on the Shore	58	Traditional	s, (d) r m f Descant: d m f s l	*do* tetrachord + *s,*	4/4	♩ /♩ /♩/♪ ♪	■ quodlibet ■ descant ■ sequence ■ I and V7 harmony ■ verses
Searching for Lambs	95	English folk-song	m s (l) t d' r' m'	Aeolian (no *f*)	5/4 (3/4)	♩ /♩ /♩/♫ /-	■ change of time ■ verses ■ ♩ upbeat

115

Title	Page	Origin	Solfa	Mode	Time	Rhythm	Features
Senua de Dende	17	Ghanaian	(d) r m f s l t d'	Major	4/4	♩	• two-part canon • ostinato • A A B
Si Si Si	69	Congolese folk-song	(d) r m f s l t d'	Major	4/4	♩	• part-singing • body percussion and movement • A B C
Sing Together Merrily	14	Traditional	(s,) t, d r m f s	Major (no l)	6/8	♩	• five-part round • sequence • second inversion of tonic chord
Sleigh Song	52	Russian	m, s, si,(l,) t, d r m f s	Aeolian (+ si)	2/4	♩	• verse and chorus • two-part • A B C C
Solfa Canon	15	Lajos Bárdos	(d) r m f s l t d'	Major	4/4	♩	• two-part canon • solfa only
Solfège Round	15	Anonymous	d r m f s l ta t (d')	Major	3/4	♩	• two-part canon • ♩ upbeat • solfa only • stick notation
Step Back Baby	56	American traditional	m s (l)	la tritonic	4/4	♩	• quodlibet • movement
Sweep Away	5	American traditional	s, (d) r m s l	do pentatonic	4/4	♩	• internal upbeat • A B C D D • canon • legato singing

Title	Page	Origin	Solfa	Tonality	Time	Rhythm	Features
The Sweet Nightingale	91	English folk-song	s, l, t, (d) r m f s l	Major	**3/4**	*(rhythm notation)*	■ verse and refrain ■ role play ■ sequence ■ legato singing ■ ♫ upbeat
This Old Man	26	Traditional	(d) r m f s l	*do* hexachord	**2/4**	*(rhythm notation)*	■ two-part ■ I IV and V harmony ■ A B C D melody ■ stick notation
Turn the Glasses Over	60	Virginian folk-song	s, l, (d) r m s l	*do* pentatonic	**2/4**	*(rhythm notation)*	■ quodlibet ■ ostinatos ■ augmentation ■ dance
Tzena Tzena	72	Israeli folk-song	(d) r m f s l t d' r'	Major	**4/4**	*(rhythm notation)*	■ three-part round ■ movement/dance
Vem Kan Segla Förutan Vind?	51	Swedish folk-song	m, si, (l,) t, d r m f s l	Melodic minor (no *fi*)	**6/8**	*(rhythm notation)*	■ optional canon ■ ostinatos ■ Swedish text
Viva la Musica	19	Michael Praetorius	f, (s,) l, t, d r m f s	Mixolydian	**4/4**	*(rhythm notation)*	■ three-part canon
Walk Along Joe	30	American folk-song	s, l, (d) r m s l	*do* pentatonic	**2/4**	*(rhythm notation)*	■ two-part ■ A B C C melody ■ ostinato
Way Down Yonder in the Cornfields	29	Traditional	s, l, ta, t, (d) r m f s	Major + *ta*	**2/4**	*(rhythm notation)*	■ two-part ■ humour

Song	Page	Source	Solfa	Mode	Time	Rhythm	Features
Weevily Wheat	76	American traditional	s, l, (d) r m s l	*do* pentatonic	2/4		■ A B A C ■ canon ■ ostinatos ■ humour
Who Stole my Chickens?	7	Traditional	(d) r m f s l	*do* hexachord	4/4		■ A Av B C ■ humour ■ internal upbeat ■ text variation
Wo-ye-le	32	Josef Marais (based on canoe paddlers' chant)	s, (l,) d r m s l	*la* pentatonic	6/8		■ two-part ■ rhythmic ostinato

This book is printed on acid-free paper.

British Kodály Academy
13 Midmoor Road
London
SW19 4JD

07 06 05 04 03

First Published 2000
2nd Edition Reprint 2007

ISBN 0-9512592-4-5

Original drawings by Art graduates Hannah Dodds and FloraMay Waterhouse, and by Jessica Waterhouse (aged 11).

Cover Illustrations: FloraMay Waterhouse and Hannah Dodds

Typeset by Nick Price at Note-orious Productions Ltd, London
Printed in Great Britain by Wellington Press, Sutton, Surrey

Appendix 1
Outline of National Curriculum / QCA Guidelines and Related Songs

Chapter topics shown below are a useful starting point in helping teachers choose songs from the book. Every chapter begins with a brief introduction on the general purpose and use of the repertoire. Teachers should also study the Teaching Tips with any chosen song, for guidance on how it can be used to fulfil particular learning objectives.

Unit numbers below are taken from the QCA/DfES Scheme of Work for Keystages 1 and 2. Although the Ongoing Skills Units 1, 8 and 15 include singing throughout the year, some of the Units are more specifically designed for instrumental work, and have therefore not been included. The suggested songs for Keystage 3 provide ongoing skills for Years 7 and 8 and will enhance lessons in composition, form, ICT and other Keystage requirements.

Listening, aural memory and the Kodály approach

Following a Kodály approach at Keystages 1 and 2, all songs are taught initially by rote, and children learn through listening, imitation and repetition. This develops listening skills, concentration and aural memory for both words and music as a matter of course, and fulfils the following important Keystage criteria:

- At KS1 children will listen carefully and develop aural memory (Unit 1).
- At KS2, songs may be longer and musically more complex. Children will thus further develop aural memory and concentration, listen with greater attention to detail (Unit 8), and remember longer pieces of music (Unit 15).

Note on performing

It is assumed that 'performing' is not limited to formal performance. All the songs in the book can be used for groups to perform to each other, and class singing to performance standard, as a regular part of classroom music. Choice of appropriate material will depend on the age and stage of the children.

Learning Objectives

Keystage 1

Suggested Songs (Chapter and Page Number)

Recommended Chapters:

1 2 3 5 7

Unit 1: Ongoing Skills For Keystage 1

To find singing voice	**1** 2 3 4 6 7 **2** 11 13 **3** 22 24 **5** 38 41 **7** 57 58 62
To develop awareness of phrase	**1** 2 3 4 6 7 **5** 38 41 **7** 57 58
To sing with others	**1** 2 3 4 6 7 **2** 11 13 **3** 22 24 **5** 38 41 **7** 57 58 62
To control pulse and rhythm	**1** 2 3 4 6 **7** 5 38 41 **7** 57 58
To control pitch	**1** 4 6 7 **2** 11 13 **3** 22 **5** 38 41 **7** 57 58
To control expressive elements, eg timbre, dynamics, tempo	**1** 6 7 **2** 11 **3** 22 **7** 57 58
To listen carefully and develop aural memory	see page 119

Other Units For Keystage 1

Unit 2: To explore different sound sources	**5** 35 See Also Unit 1: To find singing voice
Unit 3: Exploring duration	**1** 2 3 4 6 7 **5** 38 41 **7** 57 58
Unit 4: Exploring pulse and rhythm	**1** 2 3 4 6 7 **5** 38 41 **7** 57 58
Unit 5: Exploring pitch	**1** 4 6 7 **2** 11 13 **3** 22 **5** 38 41 **7** 57 58
Unit 7: Exploring timbre, tempo and dynamics	**1** 6 7 **2** 11 **3** 22 **7** 57 58

Keystage 2 (Years 3 & 4)

Recommended Chapters:

1 2 3 4 5 6 7 9

Unit 8: Ongoing Skills For Keystage 2 (Years 3 & 4)

To listen with attention to detail and develop aural memory	see page 119
To develop singing voice	**1** 2 - 7 **2** 11 12 13 14 17 18 **3** 21 - 24 **4** 30 **5** 36 38 39 40 41 42 43 45 **6** 47 **7** 56 - 64 **9** 76 78 79
To use thinking voice	**1** 6 **3** 21 22 **5** 42 **7** 56
To develop control of pulse and rhythm	**1** 2 3 4 6 7 **2** 11 14 17 18 **3** 21 23 24 **4** 30 **5** 36 38 39 40 41 42 43 45 **7** 56 - 64 **9** 76 78 79
To develop awareness of simple structures (phrases)	**1** 2 - 7 **2** 11 - 14 17 18 **3** 21 23 24 **4** 30 **5** 36 40 41 42 43 45 **7** 56 - 64 **9** 76 78 79
To recognise and control pitch / about staff notation	**1** 4 5 **2** 11 13 14 17 18 **3** 21 **4** 30 **5** 36 38 39 41 42 43 45 **7** 56 - 64 **9** 76 79
To express the meaning of songs	**1** 5 7 **2** 17 **3** 22 **5** 43 **7** 56 57 **9** 78 79
To respond to structure in music through movement and dance	**1** 1 2 3 6 **3** 21 24 **5** 35-45 **6** 50 **7** 56 57 60 **8** 69 72 **9** 79 **10** 88

Other Units For Keystage 2 (Years 3 & 4)

Unit 10: Exploring rhythmic patterns	**1** 2 - 7 **2** 11 - 14 17 18 **3** 21 - 24 **4** 30 **5** 36 38 39 40 - 43 45 **7** 56 - 64 **9** 76 78 79
Unit 11: Exploring arrangements, accompanying songs	**5** 36 40 41 43 **7** 57 - 64 **9** 76 78
Unit 12: Exploring pentatonic scales	**1** 2 5 **2** 13 17 **3** 23 **4** 30 **5** 36 39 40 41 43 **7** 57 60 **9** 76
Unit 14: Exploring singing games (and dances)	**1** 2 3 4 7 **2** 13 **3** 21 24 **5** 36 38 40 41 42 43 45 **7** 56 60 62 **9** 79

Keystage 2 (Years 5 & 6)

Recommended Chapters: **All**

Unit 15: Ongoing Skills For Keystage 2 (Years 5 & 6)

To listen with sustained concentration; to remember longer pieces of music   See page 119

To learn about breathing, dynamics and accuracy of pitch   **1** 5 7 **2** 11 - 14 16 - 19 **3** 22 23 **4** 27 - 33 **5** 36 38 44 45 **6** 47 - 54 **7** 56 60 62 64 **8** 66 - 73
9 75 - 78 80 81 83 84 **10** 87 88 92 93 96 98 100

To improve tone production, diction and other vocal techniques   **1** 4 5 7 8 9 **2** 11 - 14 17 - 19 **3** 23 **4** 28 - 31 33 **5** 43 - 45 **6** 47 48 51 - 54 **7** 56 60 62 64
8 66 - 73 **9** 75 - 78 80 81 83 84 **10** 87 88 92 93 96 98 100

To learn about pulse, rhythm and metre   **1** 3 4 7 8 9 **2** 11 - 19 **3** 21 23 **4** 26 - 29 30 33 **5** 35 - 39 41 - 45 **6** 47 48 50 - 54 **7** 56 60 62 64
8 66 - 73 **9** 75 - 78 80 81 83 84 **10** 87 88 92 93 96 98 100

To learn about phrase and other musical structures   **1** 3 4 7 8 9 **2** 11 - 14 16 - 19 **3** 21 - 23 **4** 26 - 30 33 **5** 35 - 38 41 - 45 **6** 47 48 50 - 54 **7** 56 60 62 64
8 66 - 73 **9** 75 - 78 80 81 83 84 **10** 87 88 92 93 96 98 100

To extend control and understanding of pitch, including staff notation   **1** 4 5 7 8 9 **2** 11 - 15 17 - 19 **3** 21 **4** 26 28 29 30 33 **5** 36 41 43 **6** 47 - 49 51 54 **7** 62 64 **8** 66 - 73
9 75 - 78 80 81 **10** 87 92 93 98 100

To make expressive use of elements and techniques and develop performances   **1** 7 **2** 14 16 **3** 21 - 23 **4** 26 - 33 **5** 36 43 45 **6** 50 - 52 54 **7** 60 62 **8** 66 - 73 **9** 75 - 78 80 81 83 84
10 87 88 92 93 96 98 100

To respond physically to music with understanding of musical features, including metre   **1** 2 3 **5** 35-45 **6** 50 **7** 56 60 **8** 69 72 **9** 79 **10** 88

Other Units For Keystage 2 (Years 5 & 6)

Unit 16: Exploring rhythms and pulse   **1** 3 4 8 9 **2** 13 17 **3** 23 **4** 26 30 - 32 **5** 35 - 37 39 41 - 45 **6** 50 53 **7** 56 60 64 **8** 69 72 **9** 75 76 78 80 81
10 88 92 93 98

Unit 17: Exploring rounds 2-part rounds   **2** 15 17 **5** 35 43 **6** 49 - 51 53 **7** 57 60 62 **9** 75 - 77 79

3-part rounds   **2** 11 - 13 16 - 19 **5** 43 **6** 47 48 **8** 66 - 68 70 72

4-part rounds   **2** 11 - 13 17 **5** 43 **6** 47 48 **8** 68

5-part rounds   **2** 14

Unit 19: Exploring lyrics and melody   **1** 5 7 **2** 11 **6** 54 **8** 70 73 **9** 81 84 **10** 87 92 93 96 100

Unit 20: Performing together   **All** See **Note on performing** page 119

Keystage 3

Recommended Chapters: **All**

Controlling sounds through singing and playing   **1** 8 9 **2** 11 - 19 **3** 23 **4** 28 29 31 - 33 **5** 35 37 **6** 47 - 49 51 - 54 **7** 60 62 **8** 66 - 73 **9** 75 77 80 - 84
10 87 90 - 96 98 100

Appendix 2
Alphabetical Index of Songs relating to National Curriculum and QCA Guidelines

Title	Page	Units
L'il Liza Jane	60	1 8 10 11 12 14 15 16 20 KS3
London Bridge	58	1 3 4 5 7 8 10 11 20
Love Grows Under	44	1 8 15 16 20 KS3
Love Somebody	2	1 3 4 8 10 12 14 15
Ma Ma Will You Buy Me A Banana?	24	1 8 10 14
Migildi Magildi	88	15 16 20 KS3
Missa Ram Goat	23	8 10 12 15 16 20 KS3
Mr Scarfe's Action Round	37	1 8 15 16 20 KS3
Morag's Cradle Song	100	15 19 20 KS3
Mosquito Song	47	8 15 17 KS3
Mountain Hike	27	15 KS3
The Mountains I Love	73	15 19 20 KS3
No Need to Hurry	64	8 10 11 15 16 20
Oh No John	87	15 19 20 KS3
Oi Dana	7	1 3 4 5 7 8 10 14 15 19 20
Oncorrianda	39	1 8 10 12 15 16
One' These Fine Mornings	75	15 16 17 20 KS3
My Owlet	57	1 3 4 5 7 8 10 11 12 20
The Poor Stranger	81	15 16 19 20 KS3
Poor Wayfaring Stranger	82	20 KS3
Praise Him	17	8 10 12 15 16 17 20
Rainbow Girl	53	15 16 17 KS3
Rhythm Canon	35	1 8 15 16 17 KS3
Rhythm Machine	35	1 8 15 16 17 KS3
Rise Up O Flame	48	15 17 20 KS3
Rockin' By the Baby	57	1 3 4 5 7 8 10 11 12 20
Rumanian Canon	48	15 17 20 KS3
Salut, Ça Va?	5	8 10 15 20
Seagull Sit on the Shore	58	1 3 4 5 7 8 10 11 20
Searching for Lambs	95	20 KS3
Senua De Dende	17	15 16 17 20 KS3
Si Si Si	69	15 16 20 KS3
Sing Together Merrily	14	8 10 15 17 KS3
Sleigh Song	52	15 20 KS3
Solfa Canon	15	15 17 20 KS3
Solfège Round	15	15 17 20 KS3
Step Back Baby	56	8 10 14 15 16 20
Sweep Away	5	8 10 12 14 15 19 20 KS3
The Sweet Nightingale	91	20 KS3
This Old Man	26	15 16
Turn the Glasses Over	60	1 8 10 11 12 14 15 16 20 KS3
Tzena Tzena	72	15 16 20 KS3
Vem Kan Segla Förutan Wind?	51	15 17 KS3
Viva la Musica	19	15 17 20 KS3
Walk Along Joe	30	8 10 12 15 16 20
Way Down Yonder in the Cornfields	29	15 20 KS3
Weevily Wheat	76	8 10 11 12 15 16 17 20
Who Stole my Chickens?	7	1 3 4 5 7 8 10 14 20
Wo-ye-le	32	15 16 20 KS3